ADVANCED MATHS FOR AQA

Mechanics

Brian Jefferson

M1

Course consultant: Brian Gaulter

Coursework guidance: Craig Simms

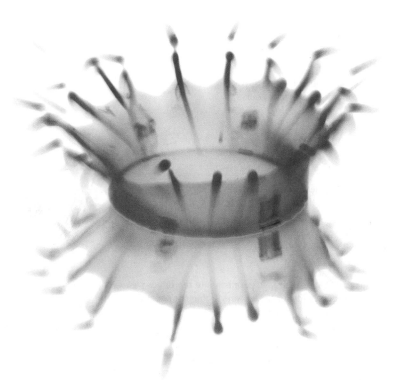

OXFORD

UNIVERSITY PRESS

Great Clarendon Street, Oxford OX2 6DP

Oxford University Press is a department of the University of Oxford.
It furthers the University's objective of excellence in research, scholarship,
and education by publishing worldwide in

Oxford   New York

Auckland   Cape Town   Dar es Salaam   Hong Kong   Karachi
Kuala Lumpur   Madrid   Melbourne   Mexico City   Nairobi
New Delhi   Shanghai   Taipei   Toronto

With offices in

Argentina   Austria   Brazil   Chile   Czech Republic   France   Greece
Guatemala   Hungary   Italy   Japan   South Korea   Poland   Portugal
Singapore   Switzerland   Thailand   Turkey   Ukraine   Vietnam

Oxford is a registered trade mark of Oxford University Press
in the UK and in certain other countries

British Library Cataloguing in Publication Data

Data available

ISBN 978 0 19 914938 4

10   9   8   7

Typeset by Tech-Set Ltd, Gateshead, Tyne and Wear
Printed and bound in Great Britain by Bell and Bain.

Paper used in the production of this book is a natural, recyclable product made
from wood grown in sustainable forests. The manufacturing process conforms
to the environmental regulations of the country of origin.

Acknowledgements

The publishers would like to thank AQA for their kind permission to reproduce past
paper questions. AQA accept no responsibility for the answers to the past paper
questions, which are the sole responsibility of the publishers.

The publishers would also like to thank James Nicholson for his authorative guidance
in preparing this book.

The image on the cover is reproduced courtesy of Adam Hart-Davis/Science Photo
Library.

Mixed Sources

Product group from well-managed
forests and other controlled sources
www.fsc.org   Cert no. TT-COC-002769
© 1996 Forest Stewardship Council

FSC

About this book

This Advanced level book is designed to help you to get your best possible grade in the AQA MM1 (A and B) module for first examination in 2005. This module can contribute to an award in GCE AS level Mathematics or A level Mathematics.

Each chapter starts with an overview of what you are going to learn and a list of what you should already know. The 'Before you start' section contains 'Check in' questions, which will help to prepare you for the topics in the chapter.

You should know how to ...	Check in
1 Manipulate vectors.	**1** Given $\mathbf{u} = 4\mathbf{i} + 7\mathbf{j}$ and $\mathbf{v} = 2\mathbf{i} + 5\mathbf{j}$, find $\mathbf{p}$ if $3\mathbf{p} = 4\mathbf{u} - 2\mathbf{v}$.

M1

Key information is highlighted in the text so you can see the facts you need to learn.

In general, $k\mathbf{a}$ is a vector parallel to $\mathbf{a}$ and with magnitude $k|\mathbf{a}|$.

Worked examples showing the key skills and techniques you need to develop are shown in boxes. Also hint boxes show tips and remainders you may find useful.

Example 5

A car, travelling at 15 m s^{-1}, suddenly accelerates at 3 m s^{-2}. What is its speed after 5 seconds?

You have $u = 15 \text{ m s}^{-1}$, $a = 3 \text{ m s}^{-2}$ and $t = 5 \text{ s}$.
You need to find v.

The formula containing these variables is $v = u + at$.

Substituting the known values gives:

$$v = 15 + 3 \times 5 = 30$$

So, the car's speed after 5 seconds is 30 m s^{-1}.

> You should write down the values that you know.

The questions are carefully graded, with lots of basic practice provided at the beginning of each exercise.

At the end of an exercise, you will sometimes find underlined questions.

13 A particle of weight W is attached by a light inextensible string of length a to a point A on a vertical wall. The particle is supported in equilibrium by a light rigid strut of length b attached to a point B on the wall at a distance a vertically below A. Show that the tension in the string is W and find the thrust in the rod.

These are optional questions that go beyond the requirements of the specification and are provided as a challenge.

At the end of each chapter, there is a summary. The 'You should now know' section is useful as a quick revision guide, and each 'Check out' question identifies important techniques that you should remember.

You should know how to ...	Check out
1 Find the components of velocity for a projectile.	**1** A particle is projected at an angle α to the horizontal and with speed u. Write down its horizontal and vertical components of velocity and displacement at time t.

M1

Following the summary, you will find a revision exercise with past paper questions from AQA. These will enable you to become familiar with the style of questions you will see in the exam.

A special feature of the text is the reference to a number of spreadsheets, used to analyse the data from suggested experiments or to explore the implications of certain models. These can be downloaded from the Oxford University Press website:

   (*http://www.oup.co.uk/secondary/mechanics*)

Practice Papers, written by a senior examiner, will directly help you to prepare for your exams.

The book also contains a chapter devoted to coursework guidance for students taking Unit MM1A. Written by a senior moderator, this section allows you to understand the requirements and to fully prepare for the coursework component.

At the end of the book, you will find numerical answers and a list of formulae you need to learn.

Contents

M1

1 Modelling

This chapter will show you how to

◆ Apply the modelling cycle in mechanics
◆ Decide which factors can be disregarded when modelling a situation
◆ Identify the modelling assumptions in solving mechanics problems

A group of people on holiday with Explorer Tours proposes to drive directly across a stretch of the Libyan Desert from their present position A to a camp site at B, on the edge of an oasis. They consult their map of the region (scale 1 cm : 1 km), which clearly marks A and B, to decide how far they will need to drive.

They measure the straight line AB on their map with a ruler and find it to be 18.6 cm. They conclude that they will need to drive 18.6 km.

When they reach B, they check the distance they have travelled and find that it is 19.2 km.

1.1 Modelling reality

These people are following a process which is fundamental to the application of mathematics to real problems.

◆ They start with the real problem …

> How far will we drive in going from A to B?

◆ They set up a mathematical model …

> The line AB on the map is a scale drawing of the journey.

◆ From this model they obtain a solution to the problem.
◆ They then check their solution against reality.

Simplifying assumptions

In setting up the model, the group make three simplifying assumptions.

◆ The model assumes that the journey is flat. That is, that any extra distance caused by hills and valleys is insignificant in relation to the length of the journey. The model would therefore tend to underestimate the actual distance to be driven.

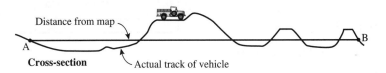

Distance from map

A
Cross-section ⌐ Actual track of vehicle
B

◆ The model assumes that the journey is in an exact straight line. In practice, it is likely that there are rocks and other obstacles which they need to circumvent. So, again, the model is likely to produce an underestimate.

◆ The model assumes that the journey is so short that they can safely ignore any distortions caused by the fact that the line AB on the map is a flat projection of a journey taking place on the curved surface of the Earth.

> All map projections distort shapes and distances, the nature of the distortion depending on the particular method of projection used.

Comparison with reality: errors

Having solved their model, the group make the journey. To compare their solution with the actual distance travelled, they need to be aware of the sources of error, both in their prediction and in their measurement of reality.

◆ Their measurement of AB on the map is at best correct to one decimal place. This would place their predicted distance, D_P km, in the interval $18.55 \leqslant D_P < 18.65$. In addition, identifying their starting and finishing points on the map could only be approximate, perhaps extending the error bounds to $18.5 \leqslant D_P < 18.7$.

◆ They find the actual distance using the odometer on their vehicle. This displays 24 924.6 km at the start and 24 943.8 km at the end of their journey. These values were truncated (rounded down) to the nearest decimal place below, which would put the start reading, S km, and the finish reading, F km, in the intervals $24\,924.6 \leqslant S < 24\,924.7$ and $24\,943.8 \leqslant F < 24\,943.9$ respectively.

◆ So, the minimum value of $(F - S)$ is $24\,943.8 - 24\,924.7 = 19.1$ km and its maximum value is $24\,943.9 - 24\,924.6 = 19.3$ km. The actual distance, D_A km, would therefore have error bounds $19.1 \leqslant D_A < 19.3$.

> Even this assumes that the inevitable inaccuracy in the odometer mechanism was small enough to be insignificant over a short journey.

Is the model good enough?

Once the errors have been quantified as far as possible, the group is able to decide whether their model is a sufficiently accurate representation of reality for their purpose. If not, they will need to re-examine the assumptions they made and modify the model. They might, for example, be able to obtain a larger-scale map and measure a route including detours around likely obstacles.

> Simplifying assumptions should make a problem less complex. However, they also create inaccuracy. Both of these factors should be considered when deciding whether to build in an assumption.

1.2 The modelling process

All applications of mathematics to real-world problems follow the same process.

1 **Specify the real problem** This should be a clear statement of the situation and should specify the results required in the solution.

2 **Make simplifying assumptions** All the factors which might affect the result should be considered and a decision made as to which should be taken into account in the model and which should be ignored. You may also make assumptions about the way in which certain variables are related.

> For example, you might decide to assume that air resistance is proportional to velocity.

3 **Set up the mathematical model** In the example given, this was a scale drawing, but it would more usually be a set of equations describing the behaviour of the simplified system.

4 **Solve the mathematical model** The equations should be solved to obtain the outcome which would result from the simplified system.

5 **Decide what really happens** This may involve setting up an experiment or obtaining data from published sources.

M1

6 **Quantify the likely errors** There may be errors in the values used in the model and/or in the results obtained from the experiment. Error bounds should be established for all such values and the effects on the outcome should be quantified.

7 **Compare with reality** The results from the model should be compared with those obtained in reality to decide if the model provides a sufficiently accurate representation of the real situation. Errors need to be taken into account in this comparison.

8 **Modify the model** If the model does not give an adequate representation of the real situation, you need to re-examine the assumptions on which it was based. A new model should then be set up to allow for the effect of one or more of the factors which had previously been ignored. The whole process should then be repeated, perhaps several times, until a sufficiently accurate model is obtained.

This process is summarised in the flowchart.

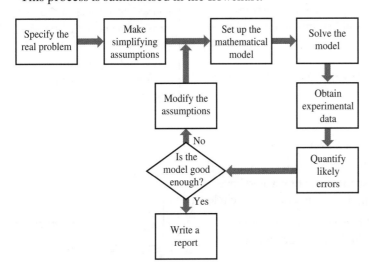

This book concentrates on problems involving forces and the motion of objects, but the process of mathematical modelling is common to all situations in which mathematics is applied to real-world problems.

> The modelling cycle forms the basis for the coursework tasks for those students doing option A. Coursework is explored fully in Chapter 7.

1.3 Modelling motion

Imagine that you want to model the motion of a person skipping.

Specifying the problem and simplifying the assumptions

You first need to state the precise questions which you want to answer, for example:

M1

✦ What is the relationship between the speed of the rope and the height of the jump?
✦ Are there limitations on these quantities for a given person and rope?

Your next task is to list all the factors which you think might have a bearing on the problem. This list can be as long as you like. It is better to include something a bit daft than to fail to take account of an important factor. Here is a possible list – you can probably think of several more items.

> Length of rope
> Mass of rope
> Flexibility of rope
> Thickness of rope
> Whether the rope drags on the ground
> Gravity
> Height of person
> Mass of person
> Size of feet, length of arms and other physical proportions
> Movement of arms and therefore establishing the locus of rope
> Speed of rope
> Height of jump
> Amount of time feet need to stay in contact with the ground in the jumping process
> Air resistance
> How 'bouncy' the ground is

Once you have your list, you must decide what assumptions to make.

You can begin to quantify the variables: for example, there would be a lower limit on the rate of skipping because the value of v would have be great enough to prevent the rope going slack at the top of the circle.

> You will need to decide how to measure the height of jumps. For example, it could be the gap between the feet and the ground, or the movement of the person's centre of gravity.

There would also be an upper limit on v because time would be needed for the person to get sufficiently high off the ground to allow the passage of the rope.

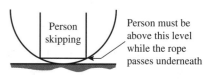

Setting up and solving the mathematical model

For a first, simple model you might decide that a rope, which is curved and has mass all the way along, is too complex. It would be easier mathematically to replace it with a thin, rigid rod attached to two strings of negligible mass. In addition, it would be simpler if you supposed that the rope is being made to rotate at a constant speed in a circle around a fixed point in space, with the ground being a tangent to the circle.

The simplest way to model the person would be as a cuboid of uniformly dense material rising and falling without any change of shape. The cuboid would spend a fixed proportion of each cycle in contact with the ground and the rest moving vertically under gravity.

In this model, any resistance to the motion of the rope or the person would be ignored.

The important variables are:

◆ The length, r, of the strings.
◆ The speed, v, of the rod around the circle.
◆ The height, h, of the jump.
◆ The time, t, from the start of the motion.
◆ The proportion, p, of time spent in contact with the ground.

You can write equations connecting r, v, h, p and t, which would form the model. By manipulating these equations, you could find solutions predicting the position of the rope and the person for any value of t.

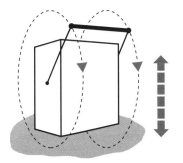

You will need to make assumptions such as the rope is at the bottom of the circle when the person is at the top of the jump.

M1

Deciding what really happens and modifying the model

Your task would now be to observe people skipping, first to decide on a reasonable value for p and then to test out the predictions of your model about the relation between the height of jump and the speed of the rope.

It is unlikely that the model would be very good, so you would need to reassess your assumptions. Observing skippers would help you to decide which assumptions to modify. You would continue to refine your model and test it against observation until you regarded the predictions as sufficiently accurate.

1.4　Conventional terms

When problems are stated mathematically, terms are often used which imply that certain assumptions are being made. For example, you will see questions referring to a string as *light*. This would indicate that the mass of the string is sufficiently small for it to be ignored.

The common terms used in Mechanics are given in the table below.

Term	Applies to	What is disregarded
Inextensible	Strings, rods	Stretching
Thin	Strings, rods	Diameter, thickness
Light	Strings, springs, rods	Mass
Particle	Object of negligible size	Rotational motion, size
Rigid	Rods	Bending
Small	Object of negligible size	Rotational motion
Smooth	Surfaces, pulleys	Friction

M1

Summary

You should know how to ...	Check out
1 Decide the reasons for using modelling to solve mechanics problems.	**1** A person swims across a river. Why would the mathematical model assume that the river flows at a constant speed?
2 Identify modelling assumptions made in exercise and examination questions.	**2** A shell is fired from a gun. What assumptions should be made in determining its flight?

Revision exercise 1

1 Do you think it would be reasonable to disregard air resistance in the following situations?

a) A marble dropped from an upstairs window.

b) A table tennis ball dropped from an upstairs window.

c) A marble dropped from an aircraft at 2000 metres altitude.

d) A shot being putt.

e) A rocket firework being set off.

f) A child on a swing.

g) A person walking.

h) A person cycling.

2 Do you think it would be reasonable to disregard friction in the following situations?

a) Skiing downhill.

b) A child going down a slide.

c) Raising an object on a rope passing over a tree branch.

d) Raising an object on a rope passing over a pulley.

e) A car being driven in a straight line.

f) A car being driven round a curve.

3 In the sport of bungee jumping, participants jump from a platform with an elastic rope attached to their ankles. The other end of the rope is attached to the platform.

Participants free fall until the elastic stretches. The tension built up in the elastic slows them down and eventually brings them to a temporary stop. Often the jump takes place over water and the participants have the choice of whether to come to a stop before they hit the water, whether to get their hair wet or whether to plunge into the water to a depth chosen by them.

The problem is to work out the correct length of rope to satisfy their desires.

In modelling this problem, this list of factors was drawn up.

a) The weight of the person.

b) The height of the person.

c) The height of the platform.

d) The elasticity of the bungee rope.

e) The number of ropes used.

f) The accuracy with which the measurements can be made.

g) The weight of the bungee rope.

h) The weather conditions.

i) The depth of the water.

j) The style of jumping.

k) Air resistance.

l) The clothing worn.

m) The maximum stress the body can take.

n) The way the bungee rope deforms when it is stretched.

o) How fast the water is flowing.

p) How fast the person wants to be moving when he/she hits the water.

q) Whether there is a cross wind.

r) How the rope is tied to the ankles.

s) Any more you can think of.

Separate these factors into three lists:

A Those which can be totally ignored in forming a mathematical model.

B Those which cannot be ignored but which you think would be too difficult to include in an initial model.

C Those which should probably be included in an initial model.

In each case, try to justify your inclusion of each item in its list.

M1

4 For each of the following situations, make a list of the factors which you think might have an influence on the outcome.

a) The amount of water falling on a person crossing an open space in the rain.

b) The motion of a boat crossing a river.

c) A tennis player serving.

d) A toy car free-wheeling from rest down a slope.

e) A child swinging on a rope tied to a tree branch.

M1

2 Kinematics in one and two dimensions

This chapter will show you how to

- ◆ Distinguish between a vector quantity and a scalar quantity
- ◆ Calculate average speed and velocity
- ◆ Draw and interpret graphs of displacement, velocity and acceleration against time
- ◆ Use the constant acceleration equations, including the motion of a particle moving vertically under gravity
- ◆ Manipulate vectors in two dimensions
- ◆ Find and use the components of a vector
- ◆ Analyse two-dimensional motion with constant acceleration

M1

Before you start

You should know how to ...	Check in
1 Find the gradient of a straight line.	**1** Find the gradient of the line through the points $(1, 4)$ and $(3, 10)$.
2 Substitute in an algebraic equation.	**2** In the equation $s = ut + \frac{1}{2}at^2$, find s when $u = 10$, $t = 4$ and $a = 6$.
3 Solve a quadratic equation by use of the formula.	**3** Find x when $x^2 - 3x - 1 = 0$.
4 Use Pythagoras's theorem.	**4** Here is a right-angled triangle, ABC. 2 cm, 5 cm Find the length AB.
5 Use trigonometry in a right-angled triangle.	**5** a) Find angle CAB in Question 4. b) In the triangle below, find: i) the length DE; ii) the length EF. 40°, 8 cm
6 Manipulate surds.	**6** Simplify $\sqrt{12} + \sqrt{27}$.

When modelling physical systems a number of the quantities used, such as force, displacement, velocity, acceleration and momentum, share a common property. That is, they can be specified completely only by stating **both** their **magnitude** (size) and their **direction**. Such quantities are called **vectors**.

> A vector quantity is one which has both magnitude and direction.

Also used are quantities, such as distance, speed, work and power, which are completely specified by their magnitude. Such quantities are called **scalars**.

> A scalar quantity is one which has **only magnitude**.

M1

Kinematics is the branch of mechanics which deals with motion. So, in this chapter, you will be concerned with the position, velocity and acceleration of bodies and how these change with time. You will not, at this stage, be concerned with the causes of these changes of motion.

Initially, the focus will be on motion in one dimension. This means that the direction associated with vector quantities will be indicated simply by a positive or negative sign.

2.1 Motion in one dimension

Terminology

First, you should know the terms used in kinematics.

Displacement is a vector quantity stating where an object is or how it has moved relative to some chosen point. The SI unit of displacement is metres (m). For example:

This number line shows an origin, O, and two points, P and Q.

An object moving from P to Q would undergo a displacement of 5 m. An object moving from Q to P would undergo a displacement of −5 m.

The word **position** is sometimes used for the displacement of an object from the origin. So, in the example, an object at P would have a position of −2 m.

Distance is a scalar quantity stating how far an object has travelled. This is **not** the same as displacement. For example, if on the number line above, an object moved from P to Q and then to O, it would have travelled a distance of 8 m but its resulting displacement from its starting point would be 2 m.

Velocity is a vector quantity stating how fast an object is moving, and in which direction. The SI unit of velocity is metres per second ($m\,s^{-1}$, or occasionally m/s).

> Apart from time, the characteristics of motion are vector quantities. However, sometimes the reference is just to their magnitude, and the terminology reflects this difference.

Speed is a scalar quantity stating how fast an object is moving. It is the magnitude of the velocity vector.

Acceleration is a vector quantity stating the rate of change of the velocity. The SI unit of acceleration is metres per second per second, or metres per second^2 (m s^{-2}, or occasionally m/s^2).

Average speed is defined as:

$$\text{Average speed} = \frac{\text{Distance travelled}}{\text{Time taken}}$$

Speed is usually expressed in m s^{-1}, but in some circumstances other units are used, notably kilometres per hour (km h^{-1}).

Modelling assumptions

In all discussion of one-dimensional motion, the following will be assumed:

✦ The motion takes place along a straight line (even when, say, a car journey is being considered, where the road is unlikely to be straight).

✦ All objects will be modelled as particles, thereby ignoring their size.

M1

> In your M1 examination, all questions on one-dimensional motion will make the assumption that the motion is along a straight line.

Example 1

A train travels from Penzance to Exeter. Distances from Penzance (in km) and times of arrival/departure are shown in the table. Ignoring any time spent stopped at stations, find the train's average speed for each stage and for the whole journey.

Station	Distance (km)	Time
Penzance	0	0600
Plymouth	121	0706
Exeter	195	0736

Penzance–Plymouth: Distance = 121 km, time = 66 min = 1.1 h. This gives:

$$\text{Average speed} = \frac{121}{1.1} = 110 \text{ km h}^{-1}$$

Plymouth–Exeter: Distance = 74 km, time = 30 min = 0.5 h. This gives:

$$\text{Average speed} = \frac{74}{0.5} = 148 \text{ km h}^{-1}$$

Whole journey: Distance = 195 km, time = 96 min = 1.6 h. This gives:

$$\text{Average speed} = \frac{195}{1.6} = 121.875 \text{ km h}^{-1}$$

> **Note** The average speed of a journey of several stages cannot be found by calculating the mean of the average speeds for the individual stages. In Example 1, 121.875 km h^{-1} is not the mean of 110 km h^{-1} and 148 km h^{-1}. The average speed for a journey must be found using the **total distance** and the **total time**.

Exercise 2A

1 a) Convert: i) $54 \, \text{km h}^{-1}$ to m s^{-1}; ii) $35 \, \text{m s}^{-1}$ to km h^{-1}.

  b) A car travels 150 km between 1030 am and 1220 pm.
     Find its average speed i) in km h^{-1}; ii) in m s^{-1}.

2 In a charity walk, a group walked for 2 hours, covering a distance of 6 km. They then stopped for lunch, which took another hour, and afterwards walked the final leg of 12 km in 3 hours. Find their average speed over the whole journey.

3 A canoe race takes place on a river. Competitors have to paddle downstream for 18 km and then return upstream to their starting point. A competitor takes 2 hours to complete the downstream leg and returns at 8 km per hour.

  a) Find the average speed for the downstream leg.

  b) Find the time taken for the upstream leg.

  c) Find the average speed for the whole race.

4 A car travels 2 km at an average speed of $20 \, \text{m s}^{-1}$ and a further 2 km at an average speed of $25 \, \text{m s}^{-1}$.

  a) Find the average speed for the whole journey.

  b) Explain why, having finished the first stage at $20 \, \text{m s}^{-1}$, the car could not achieve an average speed of $40 \, \text{m s}^{-1}$ for the whole journey.

5 A cyclist travels 12 km at $15 \, \text{km h}^{-1}$ and then continues for 36 minutes at $26\frac{2}{3} \, \text{km h}^{-1}$. Find her average speed a) in km h^{-1}, b) in m s^{-1}.

6 A man jogs 8 km at $6 \, \text{km h}^{-1}$, then cycles for 2 hours at $16 \, \text{km h}^{-1}$. Find his average speed a) for the first 12 km, b) for the whole journey.

7 A person drove a distance of 18 km from her home to the motorway before joining it for the rest of her journey. Her average speed for the first part of the journey was $54 \, \text{km h}^{-1}$ and her overall average speed was $80 \, \text{km h}^{-1}$. If her journey took a total of 72 minutes, find her average speed for the second part of the journey.

8 In a motor rally stage, part of the journey is through populated areas and speeds are restricted. The rest is through a forest track where there are no restrictions on speed. One competitor took 48 minutes to complete the stage at an average speed of $100 \, \text{km h}^{-1}$. The slow section of the stage took 18 minutes and the average speed for the forest section was $125 \, \text{km h}^{-1}$. Find the average speed for the slow section of the stage.

M1

2.2 Distance and displacement, speed and velocity

In the questions in Exercise 2A, you were not required to consider the direction in which motion was taking place. The canoeist in Question 3, for example, followed an 'out and back' course, while the driver in Question 7 followed a route which essentially kept going forwards.

Regarding the outward direction as positive, the driver travelled a distance of 96 km, resulting in a total displacement of +96 km (the + sign is shown here for emphasis). However, although the canoeist travelled a distance of 36 km, the total displacement was $18 + (-18) = 0$ km. The velocity was positive on the outward leg of the journey and negative on the return leg.

Average speed has been defined in terms of total distance and total time. Now **average velocity** can be defined:

$$\text{Average velocity} = \frac{\text{Total displacement}}{\text{Total time}}$$

$$= \frac{\text{Final position} - \text{Initial position}}{\text{Total time}}$$

In a similar way, **average acceleration** can be defined:

$$\text{Average acceleration} = \frac{\text{Change in velocity}}{\text{Time}}$$

$$= \frac{\text{Final velocity} - \text{Initial velocity}}{\text{Time}}$$

Uniform speed, velocity and acceleration

When an object moves a given distance in a given time, its speed may not be constant. In calculating its average speed, you are finding the constant speed necessary to achieve the same distance in the same time.

The terms **uniform speed** and **uniform velocity** are used when you can assume that the speed or velocity does not change over the period of time in which you are interested.

In a similar way, the modelling assumption can be made that a body has **uniform acceleration**.

2.3 Graphs depicting motion

Displacement–time graphs

When an object travels with uniform velocity, its displacement changes by the same amount in each time period. Drawing a graph of displacement against time will result in a straight line.

> **Remember** The modelling assumption is that journeys are along a straight line.

M1

> In the foregoing examples, the driver's average velocity would be the same as her speed, but the average velocity of the canoeist would be 0 km h^{-1}.

> In reality, objects rarely travel at a constant speed for any length of time, but the idea is a useful modelling assumption.

> The symbol s is commonly used for displacement, and the graph is sometimes called an s–t graph.

Example 2

A tiger pacing along the front of her enclosure moves in one direction at 2 m s^{-1} for 6 seconds, then turns and goes the other way at 3 m s^{-1} for 5 seconds. Represent this on a displacement–time graph.

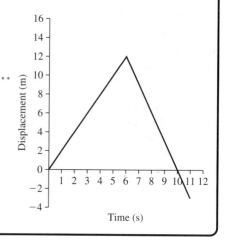

Take the first direction as positive.

The displacement is $6 \times 2 = 12 \text{ m}$ in the first stage, then $5 \times (-3) = -15 \text{ m}$ in the second stage.

This leads to the graph shown on the right.

M1

Consider the gradient of the graph in Example 2.

For the first section, using the points $(0, 0)$ and $(6, 12)$, you have:

$$\text{Gradient} = \frac{12 - 0}{6 - 0} = 2$$

In doing this, 12 metres is divided by 6 seconds, so the gradient is 2 m s^{-1}, corresponding to the tiger's velocity.

Similarly, for the second section, using the points $(6, 12)$ and $(11, -3)$, you have:

$$\text{Gradient} = \frac{-3 - 12}{11 - 6} = -3$$

This corresponds to -3 m s^{-1}, the tiger's velocity for this stage.

In general, for any straight-line displacement–time graph:

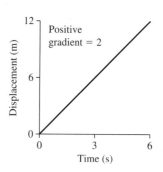

$$\text{Gradient} = \frac{\text{Change of displacement}}{\text{Time taken}} = \text{Velocity}$$

When the graph is not a straight line, the gradient of the curve at any point gives the velocity of the object at that instant.

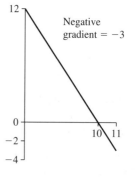

The gradient of a displacement–time graph is the velocity of the object whose motion the graph represents.

Velocity–time graphs

When an object travels with uniform acceleration, its velocity changes by the same amount in each time period. Drawing a graph of velocity against time will result in a straight line.

The symbol v is commonly used for velocity, and the graph is sometimes called a v–t graph.

This graph shows the velocity of an object (in m s⁻¹) plotted against time (in s).

$$\text{Gradient} = \frac{6 - 0}{15 - 0} = 0.4$$

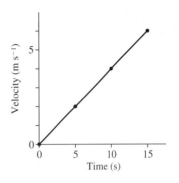

Here, 6 m s⁻¹ is divided by 15 s, so the unit for this gradient is m s⁻², which represents acceleration.

Hence, the acceleration of this object is 0.4 m s⁻². As the gradient is constant, the object is moving with uniform acceleration.

In general, for any straight-line velocity–time graph:

$$\text{Gradient} = \frac{\text{Change of velocity}}{\text{Time taken to change}} = \text{Acceleration}$$

When the graph is not a straight line, the gradient of the curve at any point gives the acceleration of the object at that instant.

The gradient of a velocity–time graph is the acceleration of the object whose motion the graph represents.

Another important property of the velocity–time graph relates to the area between the graph and the time axis.

If a cyclist travels at a uniform velocity of 8 km h⁻¹ for 3 h, the distance travelled is 24 km. The velocity–time graph is shown on the right.

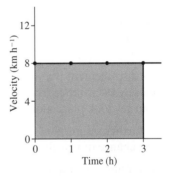

The area of the shaded rectangle is given by:

$$\text{Area} = 3 \times 8 = 24$$

The unit for this area is h × km h⁻¹ = km.

This means that the area, 24 km, represents the displacement of the cyclist from the starting point.

If the cyclist had been moving in the negative direction, the velocity would have been −8 km h⁻¹, as shown.

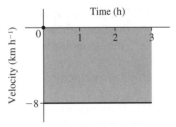

The displacement would then be:

$$\text{Area} = 3 \times (-8) = -24 \text{ km}$$

This still corresponds to the displacement. Areas below the time axis correspond to negative displacements.

It can be shown that this result also holds true for non-uniform velocity.

The area between the velocity–time graph and the time axis corresponds to the displacement of the object whose motion the graph represents.

M1

Example 3

The graph shows the displacement (in km) of a cyclist from a town A, plotted against time (in hours).

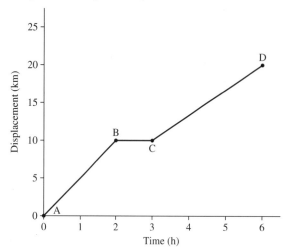

a) What assumptions have been made in drawing the graph?
b) What happened in the different stages of the journey?

a) The sections of the graph are straight and so it has been assumed that the velocity of the cyclist was uniform during each stage. (This is, of course, most unlikely in practice.)

As displacement is a vector quantity but appears on the graph merely as 'distance from A', it has also been assumed that the journey took place along a straight line.

A further assumption is that as each stage started and finished, the change of velocity was instantaneous.

> Since this is a displacement–time graph, the gradient at each point represents the velocity of the cyclist at that time.

b) Examining each section of the graph in turn, you will find:

AB The journey from A to B took 2 hours and the displacement was 10 km. The velocity of the cyclist, corresponding to the gradient of the graph, was:

$$\text{Velocity} = \frac{10}{2} = 5 \text{ km h}^{-1}$$

BC The gradient of this part of the graph is zero. The cyclist had zero velocity and so must have had an hour's rest.

CD The gradient of this section of the graph, and therefore the cyclist's velocity, was:

$$\text{Velocity} = \frac{20 - 10}{6 - 3} = 3.33 \text{ km h}^{-1}$$

Example 4

A car starts from rest at a point A and drives up a slope. It accelerates to a speed of 18 m s^{-1} in 6 s and maintains this speed for 4 s. The gears are then disengaged and the car coasts to rest with acceleration -2 m s^{-2}. Unfortunately, the driver forgets to put the handbrake on, so the car then rolls back down the slope with acceleration -1 m s^{-2}.

a) Sketch a velocity–time graph of the motion.

b) Calculate the acceleration on the first stage.

c) Find how far the car was from A when it came instantaneously to rest.

d) When will it return to A?

....

a) The graph shows the car's journey. The T represents the time at which the car returns to A.
The car takes 9 s to slow from 18 m s^{-1} to rest, corresponding to an acceleration (gradient) of 2 m s^{-2}.

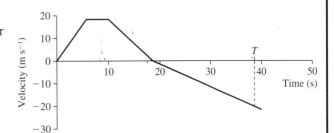

M1

b) The gradient of the line representing the first stage of the motion is:
$$\frac{18}{6} = 3 \text{ m s}^{-2}$$

c) The car comes instantaneously to rest when the velocity is zero. This happens at 19 s. The displacement of the car at that time corresponds to the area of the trapezium above the time axis. Hence, you have:
$$\text{Displacement} = \tfrac{1}{2}(19 + 4) \times 18 = 207 \text{ m}$$

d) The car returns to A when its total displacement is zero. This means that the triangular area below the time axis must be -207 m.
As the acceleration (gradient) for that stage is -1 m s^{-2}, the triangle has equal base and height, both equal to $(T - 19)$. The area is below the axis and therefore negative, so you have:
$$-\tfrac{1}{2}(T - 19)^2 = -207$$
$$(T - 19) = \sqrt{414}$$
$$T = 19 + \sqrt{414} = 39.3 \text{ s}$$

Acceleration–time graph

On some occasions, it is useful to draw an acceleration–time graph. For example, the acceleration–time graph corresponding to the velocity–time graph in Example 4 is shown on the next page.

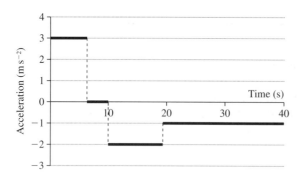

The relationship between the acceleration–time graph and the velocity–time graph is similar to that between the velocity–time graph and the displacement–time graph, namely:

Displacement–time graph	Velocity–time graph	Acceleration–time graph
Gradient = Velocity	Area = Displacement Gradient = Acceleration	Area = Velocity

If you want to get a feel for the relationship between these graphs, download the spreadsheet MOTIONGRAPHS from the OUP website. Just type in the address: http://www.oup.co.uk/secondary/mechanics

M1

Exercise 2B

1 A woman, walking a dog along a straight path, stops and releases the dog at a point A. She continues to walk forward at a constant speed of 1.4 m s^{-1}. The dog runs 100 m forward in 10 seconds, stops and sniffs for 10 seconds, then runs forward a further 50 m in 20 seconds. It then spots another dog 100 m the other side of A and runs back to join it at 5 m s^{-1}.

   a) Draw a displacement–time graph for the dog and the woman.

   b) From your graph, estimate where and when the dog passes the woman.

   c) Find the average speed and the average velocity of the dog for the whole time period described.

2 A cyclist starts, at 11 am, from town A to cycle to town B, 60 km away. In the first hour, he travels 20 km. He then rests for 15 minutes before completing the second stage of 20 km at the same speed. He then has a second 15-minute rest period before completing his final stage at the same speed as the previous two.

   a) Draw a displacement–time graph representing the journey.

   A second cyclist starts from B to cycle to A. She leaves B at the same time as the first cyclist leaves A and travels non-stop at 16 km h^{-1}.

   b) On the same axes, draw a displacement–time graph for the second cyclist, measuring the displacement of this cyclist **from A**.

   c) At what time and where do the two cyclists pass each other?

3 The displacement–time graph shows the progress of a villager doing her weekly shopping on foot.

a) Describe the motion during each stage of the journey.

b) Draw the corresponding velocity–time graph.

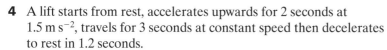

4 A lift starts from rest, accelerates upwards for 2 seconds at 1.5 m s^{-2}, travels for 3 seconds at constant speed then decelerates to rest in 1.2 seconds.

a) Sketch the velocity–time graph, stating any assumptions you have made.

b) Calculate the displacement of the lift between stops.

5 A dragonfly, at rest on a bulrush, decides to fly to a second bulrush 18 m away. It accelerates uniformly to 5 m s^{-1}, then immediately decelerates uniformly to rest on the second bulrush. Sketch the velocity–time graph and find how long the journey took.

6 A car, P, is at rest at a point O when a second car, Q, passes at a constant 20 m s^{-1}. At the moment that Q passes, P moves off in pursuit. It accelerates uniformly at 2 m s^{-2} until it reaches 30 m s^{-1}, then continues at this speed.

a) Sketch the velocity–time graph.

b) How far is P behind Q at the moment when it reaches full speed?

c) How much longer does it take for P to draw level with Q?

7 A boat starts from rest at a point A and accelerates uniformly at a rate of 0.5 m s^{-2} for 12 seconds. The propeller is then put into reverse, decelerating the boat to rest uniformly in 15 seconds. The propeller stays in reverse, making the boat accelerate back towards A. It reaches a speed of 4 m s^{-1} in 20 seconds and then continues at that speed.

a) Sketch the velocity–time graph.

b) What was the boat's greatest forward displacement from A?

c) What was the total time between the boat's leaving A and its return to A?

8 Chulchit drives to work along a straight road of length 8 km. His car accelerates and decelerates at 2.5 m s^{-2} and his preferred cruising speed is 90 km h^{-1}.

a) Assuming that he has a clear run with no hold-ups, sketch a velocity–time graph of his journey and hence calculate his journey time.

Chulchit hears on the radio that there is to be a 36 km h^{-1} speed limit for 2 km because of road works somewhere along his route, but there is no information as to where it will be.

b) Investigate the effect of the positioning of the road works on Chulchit's journey time and find his maximum and minimum best-journey times while the speed limit is in effect.

2.4 Motion with uniform acceleration

When designing mathematical models of motion, the acceleration of a body is often assumed to be uniform (constant). This simplifies the model and allows the derivation of a useful set of equations.

Suppose that a body starts with velocity u when $t = 0$, and accelerates at a uniform rate a for a time t, when its velocity has become v. Call the displacement achieved during this motion s. Usually, t is in seconds, s in metres, u and v in m s^{-1}, and a in m s^{-2}, but the equations derived will be true for any **consistent set of units**.

As the body has uniform acceleration, the velocity–time graph is a straight line (constant gradient).

The acceleration is the gradient of the graph, given by:

M1

$$\text{Gradient} = \frac{v - u}{t - 0}$$

So, you have:

$$a = \frac{v - u}{t}$$

Rearranging this equation, you get:

$$v = u + at \qquad\qquad [1]$$

The displacement is the area under the graph. The shape below the graph is a trapezium, whose area is given by:

$$\text{Area} = \tfrac{1}{2}(u + v)t$$

So, you have:

$$s = \tfrac{1}{2}(u + v)t \qquad\qquad [2]$$

From the graph, two important formulae have been derived:

$$v = u + at \qquad\qquad [1]$$
$$s = \tfrac{1}{2}(u + v)t \qquad\qquad [2]$$

These formulae can be combined to produce three further formulae covering the other possible sets of four variables.

> Notice that each formula involves four of the five variables s, u, v, a and t. Formula [1] has no s, whilst formula [2] has no a.

For example, a formula containing s, u, a and t can be produced by eliminating v from equations [1] and [2].

Substituting for v from equation [1] into equation [2], you have:

$$s = \tfrac{1}{2}(u + (u + at))t$$
$$s = ut + \tfrac{1}{2}at^2 \qquad\qquad [3]$$

Similarly, you can eliminate u, as follows:

From equation [1], you have:

$$u = v - at$$

Substituting for u in equation [2] gives:

$$s = \tfrac{1}{2}((v - at) + v))t$$
$$s = vt - \tfrac{1}{2}at^2 \qquad\qquad [4]$$

Finally, eliminate t. From equation [1], you have:

$$t = \frac{v - u}{a}$$

Substituting for t in equation [2] gives:

$$s = \tfrac{1}{2}(u + v)\left(\frac{v - u}{a}\right)$$
$$2as = (u + v)(v - u)$$

which leads to:

$$v^2 = u^2 + 2as \qquad\qquad [5]$$

These five formulae can be used to solve problems in situations where the assumption of uniform acceleration is appropriate.

In practice, some of the five formulae are used more frequently than others. Rearranged in order of usefulness, they are:

$$v = u + at$$
$$s = ut + \tfrac{1}{2}at^2$$
$$v^2 = u^2 + 2as$$
$$s = \tfrac{1}{2}(u + v)t$$
$$s = vt - \tfrac{1}{2}at^2$$

When solving problems, be systematic. Identify and list the variables with known values, and the variable which you are trying to evaluate. This will help you to decide which of the formulae to use.

M1

Note When acceleration is clearly **not uniform**, these formulae are **not valid** and should **not be used**.

You must commit these formulae to memory.

Example 5

A car travelling at 15 m s^{-1} suddenly accelerates at 3 m s^{-2}. What is its speed after 5 seconds?

··

You have $u = 15 \text{ m s}^{-1}$, $a = 3 \text{ m s}^{-2}$ and $t = 5 \text{ s}$.

You need to find v.

The formula containing these variables is $v = u + at$.

Substituting the known values gives:

$$v = 15 + 3 \times 5 = 30$$

So, the car's speed after 5 seconds is 30 m s^{-1}.

You should write down the values that you know.

Example 6

A car, travelling at 10 m s^{-1}, accelerates at 4 m s^{-2} until its speed has increased to 18 m s^{-1}. How far does it travel while accelerating?

You have $u = 10 \text{ m s}^{-1}$, $v = 18 \text{ m s}^{-1}$ and $a = 4 \text{ m s}^{-2}$. You need to find s.

The formula containing these variables is $v^2 = u^2 + 2as$.

Substituting the known values gives:

$$324 = 100 + 8s$$
$$s = 28$$

So, the distance travelled during the acceleration is 28 m.

M1

Example 7

P is a point on a slope, 10 m from the bottom. A ball is rolled up the slope from P with initial velocity 8 m s^{-1}. It undergoes a constant acceleration of -4 m s^{-2}.

a) i) How long does the ball take to reach the bottom of the slope?
   ii) How far up the slope did it travel?

b) One second after the first ball is rolled, a second ball is rolled up the slope from the bottom. It has an initial velocity of 14 m s^{-1}. Assuming that it, too, has an acceleration of -4 m s^{-2}, find when and where the two balls meet.

a) i) You know $u = 8 \text{ m s}^{-1}$, $s = -10 \text{ m}$ and $a = -4 \text{ m s}^{-2}$. You need to find t. The formula containing these variables is $s = ut + \frac{1}{2}at^2$.

   Substituting the known values gives:

   $$-10 = 8t - 2t^2$$

   Rearranging and dividing through by 2, you have:

   $$t^2 - 4t - 5 = 0$$

   which gives $t = 5$ or -1.

   In the context of the question, the negative value is inappropriate, so the ball reaches the bottom of the slope after 5 seconds.

   ii) You know $u = 8 \text{ m s}^{-1}$, $v = 0 \text{ m s}^{-1}$ and $a = -4 \text{ m s}^{-2}$. You need to find s.

   The formula containing these variables is $v^2 = u^2 + 2as$.

   Substituting the known values, you get:

   $$0 = 64 - 8s$$
   $$s = 8$$

   So, the ball comes instantaneously to rest 8 m above P.

b) Let T be the time after the release of the second ball before the balls meet. Let s_P be the displacement of the first ball above P and s_B be the displacement of the second ball above the bottom of the slope.

You know:

   First ball: $u = 8 \text{ m s}^{-1}, a = -4 \text{ m s}^{-2}, t = (T+1), s = s_P$
   Second ball: $u = 14 \text{ m s}^{-1}, a = -4 \text{ m s}^{-2}, t = T, s = s_B$

Substituting into $s = ut + \frac{1}{2}at^2$ for both balls, you get:

$$s_P = 8(T+1) - 2(T+1)^2 \qquad \text{[1]}$$
$$s_B = 14T - 2T^2 \qquad \text{[2]}$$

When the balls meet, $s_B = s_P + 10$, so you have:

$$14T - 2T^2 = 8(T+1) - 2(T+1)^2 + 10$$
$$14T - 2T^2 = 4T - 2T^2 + 16$$
$$\therefore \ T = 1.6$$

So, the balls meet 1.6 seconds after the second ball is rolled.

Substituting $T = 1.6$ into equation [2], you have:

$$s_B = 14 \times 1.6 - 2 \times 1.6^2 = 17.28$$

So, the balls meet 17.3 m above the bottom of the slope.

M1

Exercise 2C

1 A train leaves a station and accelerates uniformly at a rate of 3 m s^{-2} for 30 seconds.

   a) How far does it travel during this period?

   b) How fast is it travelling at the end of the period?

2 A stone is dropped from the top of a tower. It takes 5 seconds to reach the ground, by which time it is moving at 50 m s^{-1}.

   a) What is its acceleration?

   b) How high is the tower?

3 A body starts from rest with uniform acceleration and in 10 seconds has moved a distance of 150 m.

   a) What is its acceleration?

   b) How fast is it moving at the end of this period?

4 A train leaves a station from rest with a constant acceleration of 0.2 m s^{-2}. It reaches its maximum speed after 2 minutes and maintains this speed for a further 4 minutes, when it slows down to stop at a second station with an acceleration of -1.5 m s^{-2}. How far apart are the two stations?

5 A train accelerates uniformly from rest for 1 minute when its velocity is 30 km h^{-1}. It maintains this speed until it is 500 m from the next station when it slows down to a stop. Find the accelerations during the first and last phases of the journey.

If you need extra practice in choosing the correct equation and calculating the results, try downloading the spreadsheet SUVAT from the OUP website. Just type in the address:

http://www.oup.co.uk/secondary/mechanics

6 A car crosses a speed hump with a velocity of $4\ \text{m s}^{-1}$. It then accelerates at a rate of $2.5\ \text{m s}^{-2}$ to a speed of $9\ \text{m s}^{-1}$ when the driver applies the brakes, causing an acceleration of $-3\ \text{m s}^{-2}$, reducing the speed of the car to $4\ \text{m s}^{-1}$ to cross the next hump.

a) How far apart are the humps?

b) How long does the car take to travel from one hump to the next?

7 A moon landing craft is 1 km above the lunar surface and descending at $80\ \text{m s}^{-1}$. The rockets are then fired, giving it an upward acceleration $a\ \text{m s}^{-2}$. Find the value of a if the craft is to make a perfect soft landing.

8 A car starts from rest at the bottom of a slope. It accelerates up the slope for 8 seconds at $1.5\ \text{m s}^{-2}$, then disengages the engine and coasts. If its acceleration is now $-1\ \text{m s}^{-2}$, find the time which elapses between its leaving the bottom of the slope and returning to it.

9 A lift ascends from rest with an acceleration of $0.5\ \text{m s}^{-2}$ before slowing with an acceleration of $-0.75\ \text{m s}^{-2}$ for the next stop. If the total journey time is 10 seconds, what is the distance between the two stops?

10 Two particles, P and Q, are moving along the same line in the same direction. P is 10 m behind Q. P starts from rest and has an acceleration of $2\ \text{m s}^{-2}$. Q has a uniform velocity of $3\ \text{m s}^{-1}$.

a) How long does P take to catch Q?

b) How far has P travelled in doing so?

11 Clare is driving along a road in her car, with Henry following 40 m behind in his car. They are both travelling at $25\ \text{m s}^{-1}$. Clare spots a problem ahead, and brakes to a halt, with acceleration $-5\ \text{m s}^{-2}$. Henry takes 0.2 seconds to react, then brakes, but his brakes are less well maintained and only provide an acceleration of $-4\ \text{m s}^{-2}$. Investigate what happens.

. . . .

2.5 Free fall under gravity

A body falling through the air is subject to gravity and to air resistance.

For a small body falling at a relatively slow speed, the effect of air resistance is quite small, and so often the following modelling assumptions can be made:

✦ The body is a point mass.

✦ Air resistance can be ignored.

✦ The motion of the body is along a vertical line.

✦ The acceleration due to gravity is constant.

> Air resistance varies, depending on the shape, size and speed of the falling body. If it is included in the model, the solution of the problem can become complex.

With these assumptions, the only force acting on the body is its own weight. Its acceleration is that due to gravity. This is denoted by g and its value is usually taken to be 9.8 m s^{-2}.

Also with these modelling assumptions, the five formulae for motion with uniform acceleration are valid and can be used to solve *all* free-fall problems.

> Occasionally, you may be told to use $g = 10 \text{ m s}^{-2}$ in a specific question.

M1

Example 8

A stone is dropped from the top of a 20 m tower. After how long and with what velocity does it hit the ground?

· ·

Taking the origin as the top of the tower and downwards as the positive direction, you have $u = 0 \text{ m s}^{-1}$, $a = g = 9.8 \text{ m s}^{-2}$ and $s = 20 \text{ m}$.

To find the time, t, to reach the ground use $s = ut + \frac{1}{2}at^2$:

$$20 = \frac{1}{2} \times 9.8 \times t^2$$
$$t^2 = 4.082$$
$$t = 2.02 \text{ or } -2.02$$

In the context of the question, the negative value is inappropriate, so $t = 2.02 \text{ s}$.

To find the velocity, v, with which the stone hits the ground, use $v^2 = u^2 + 2as$.

$$v^2 = 2 \times 9.8 \times 20 = 392$$
$$v = 19.8 \text{ or } -19.8$$

In the context of the question, the negative value is inappropriate so, $v = 19.8 \text{ m s}^{-1}$.

> Having found the value of t in the first part of Example 8, you could have used as an alternative $v = u + at$ to find the value of v.

Example 9

A ball was thrown vertically upwards from ground level with a velocity of 28 m s^{-1}.

a) What was its maximum height above the ground?

b) How long did it take to return to the ground?

· ·

Taking the point from which the ball was thrown as the origin, and upwards as the positive direction, you have $u = 28 \text{ m s}^{-1}$ and $a = -g = -9.8 \text{ m s}^{-2}$.

a) At the top of the ball's flight, $v = 0 \text{ m s}^{-1}$ and $s = h \text{ m}$, the maximum height.

To find h, use $v^2 = u^2 + 2as$, which gives:

$$0 = 28^2 + 2 \times (-9.8) \times h$$
$$h = 40$$

So, the maximum height reached is 40 m.

b) When the ball returns to ground level, $s = 0$ m.

To find t, the time taken to return to ground level, use $s = ut + \frac{1}{2}at^2$, which gives:

$$0 = 28t + \frac{1}{2} \times (-9.8) \times t^2$$
$$0 = t(28 - 4.9t)$$
$$t = 0 \quad \text{or} \quad 5.71$$

In the context of the question, the solution $t = 0$ represents the time at which the ball was thrown, and the solution $t = 5.71$ represents the time at which the ball returned to ground level. So, the ball took 5.71 s to return to ground level.

M1 **Example 10**

A ball is thrown vertically upwards from ground level at 20 m s^{-1}. A boy, leaning out of a window 8 m above the point of projection, catches the ball on its way down.

a) What is the time of flight of the ball?

b) How fast is it travelling when the boy catches it?

Taking the origin to be the point of projection and upwards as the positive direction, you have $u = 20$ m s^{-1} and $a = -g = -9.8$ m s^{-2}.

a) When the ball is caught, $s = 8$ m. To find the time, t, use $s = ut + \frac{1}{2}at^2$:

$$8 = 20t + \frac{1}{2} \times (-9.8) \times t^2$$
$$4.9t^2 - 20t + 8 = 0$$

which gives:

$$t = 3.63 \quad \text{or} \quad 0.450$$

The value $t = 0.450$ s corresponds to the moment when the ball passes the boy on the way up, and $t = 3.63$ s represents the time at which he catches the ball. So, the time of flight is 3.63 s.

b) To find the velocity of the ball when it is caught, use $v = u + at$:

$$v = 20 + (-9.8) \times 3.63 = -15.6$$

So, the ball is travelling at a speed of 15.6 m s^{-1} when it is caught, with the negative symbol indicating that it is travelling downwards.

You could have used:

$$v^2 = u^2 + 2as$$

The solutions would have been $v = 15.6$ or -15.6. The positive value corresponds to the ball's velocity on the way up.

Exercise 2D

1 A stone is dropped from the top of a cliff 50 m high.

a) How long does it take to reach the beach below?

b) What is its velocity when it hits the beach?

2 A ball is thrown vertically upwards with a speed of $15\,\text{m s}^{-1}$.

  a) What will be the greatest height reached by the ball.

  b) How long does it take to reach maximum height?

  c) How long does it take to reach ground level again?

3 A ball was thrown vertically upwards. It just touched a cable $20\,\text{m}$ above the ground.

  a) What was the initial speed of the ball?

  b) How long did the ball take to reach ground level again?

  c) What was the velocity of the ball when it hit the ground?

4 A stone was thrown vertically upwards with a speed of $5\,\text{m s}^{-1}$ from the top of a cliff, $60\,\text{m}$ high, so that it fell to the beach below.

  a) What was the greatest height reached by the stone?

  b) What was the velocity of the stone when it hit the beach?

  c) How long did it take for the stone to hit the beach?

M1

5 A stone was thrown vertically upwards with a speed of $10\,\text{m s}^{-1}$. One second later, another stone was thrown vertically upwards from the same point and with the same speed.

  a) How high were the stones when they met?

  b) How long after the first stone was thrown did the stones meet?

6 A boy dropped a stone from the top of a multistorey car park. At the same time, his friend threw a second stone vertically upwards from the ground below, with a speed of $30\,\text{m s}^{-1}$. The two stones met $1.5\,\text{s}$ later. How high was the top of the car park?

7 A body falls from rest from the top of a tower. During the last second of its motion it falls $\frac{7}{16}$ of the whole distance. Show that the time taken for the descent is independent of the value of g, and find the height of the tower in terms of g.

8 A stone falls past a window, $2.5\,\text{m}$ high, in $0.5\,\text{s}$. Taking $g = 10\,\text{m s}^{-2}$, find the height from which the stone fell.

9 An object is thrown vertically downwards with speed V. During the sixth second of its motion, it travels a distance h. Find V in terms of h and g.

10 An object is projected vertically upwards with a velocity of $u\,\text{m s}^{-1}$, and after t s a second object is projected upwards from the same point and with the same velocity. Find, in terms of u, t and g, the time which elapses between the second object's projection and the collision between the objects.

2.6 Vectors in two dimensions

Before considering motion in two dimensions, you need to become familiar with the language and mathematics of vectors.

The simplest vector quantity to illustrate and work with is a displacement, or translation, by a given distance in a given direction. The mathematical techniques used with displacements will apply to *all* other vector quantities.

Notation

A displacement can be represented by a directed line segment. The line segment shown is a translation from A to B. To show that it is a translation, rather than just the distance AB, you write it as $\overrightarrow{AB}$ (it is occasionally indicated by using bold type, **AB**).

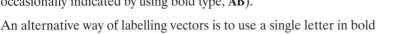

M1

An alternative way of labelling vectors is to use a single letter in bold type, such as **a**. This would be handwritten as a̲.

The magnitude of the vector $\overrightarrow{AB}$ is shown as AB or $|\overrightarrow{AB}|$.

The magnitude of the vector **a** is shown as $|\mathbf{a}|$ or a.

A vector with a magnitude of 1 is called a **unit vector**. The unit vector in the direction of a vector **a** is usually labelled **â**.

> **â** is often referred to as 'a hat'.

Properties of vectors

> Vectors are equal if and only if they have the same magnitude and direction.

For example, in the parallelogram shown on the right, $\overrightarrow{AB} = \overrightarrow{DC}$ and $\overrightarrow{AD} = \overrightarrow{BC}$.

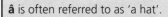

In the triangle on the right you can see that combining the translations $\overrightarrow{AB}$ and $\overrightarrow{BC}$ has the same effect as the single translation $\overrightarrow{AC}$. $\overrightarrow{AC}$ is called the **vector sum** of $\overrightarrow{AB}$ and $\overrightarrow{BC}$.

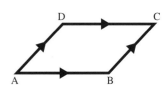

> The vector sum is written as:
> $$\overrightarrow{AB} + \overrightarrow{BC} = \overrightarrow{AC}$$
> where $\overrightarrow{AC}$ is called the **resultant** of $\overrightarrow{AB}$ and $\overrightarrow{BC}$.

> Note the use of the double arrowhead to indicate that the vector is a resultant.

The resultant of the displacements $\overrightarrow{AB}$ and $\overrightarrow{BA}$ would be a vector with zero magnitude and undefined direction. This is **0**, the **zero vector** (handwritten 0̲). It follows that, as $\overrightarrow{AB} + \overrightarrow{BA} = \mathbf{0}$, you can write $\overrightarrow{BA} = -\overrightarrow{AB}$.

> In general, the vector $-\mathbf{p}$ has the same magnitude as **p** but the opposite direction.

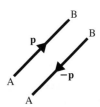

Multiplying a vector by a scalar changes its magnitude but not its direction. For example, **a** + **a** = 2**a** corresponds to the translation **a** applied twice, giving a translation twice as far in the same direction.

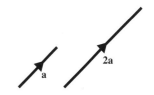

> In general, $k\mathbf{a}$ is a vector parallel to **a** and with magnitude $k|\mathbf{a}|$.

The resultant of two or more vectors is unchanged by the order in which they are applied or bracketed.

In the parallelogram ABCD:

$$\overrightarrow{AC} = \overrightarrow{AB} + \overrightarrow{BC} = \overrightarrow{AD} + \overrightarrow{DC}$$
$$\mathbf{p} + \mathbf{q} = \mathbf{q} + \mathbf{p}$$

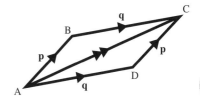

> Vector addition is **commutative**.

In the quadrilateral ABCD:

$$\overrightarrow{AD} = \overrightarrow{AC} + \overrightarrow{CD} = \overrightarrow{AB} + \overrightarrow{BD}$$
$$(\mathbf{p} + \mathbf{q}) + \mathbf{r} = \mathbf{p} + (\mathbf{q} + \mathbf{r})$$

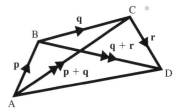

> Vector addition is **associative**.

Subtraction can now be defined.

In the triangle ABC:

$$\overrightarrow{CB} = \overrightarrow{CA} + \overrightarrow{AB}$$
$$= -\mathbf{q} + \mathbf{p}$$
$$= \mathbf{p} - \mathbf{q}$$

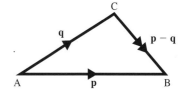

> Generally:
>
> $$\mathbf{p} - \mathbf{q} = -\mathbf{q} + \mathbf{p}$$
>
> Subtracting a vector is equivalent to adding its negative.

Example 11

In the diagram, ABEF and BCDE are squares. Vector $\overrightarrow{AB} = \mathbf{p}$ and vector $\overrightarrow{AE} = \mathbf{q}$. Find a) $\overrightarrow{AC}$, b) $\overrightarrow{AD}$, c) $\overrightarrow{AF}$, d) $\overrightarrow{EC}$.

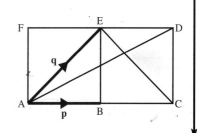

a) $\overrightarrow{AC} = 2\overrightarrow{AB}$, which gives: $\overrightarrow{AC} = 2\mathbf{p}$
b) $\overrightarrow{AD} = \overrightarrow{AE} + \overrightarrow{ED} = \mathbf{q} + \overrightarrow{ED}$
   But $\overrightarrow{ED} = \overrightarrow{AB} = \mathbf{p}$. So, you have:
     $\overrightarrow{AD} = \mathbf{q} + \mathbf{p}$

M1

Note Any route from A to D gives the required result. For example, you could have:

$$\vec{AD} = \vec{AB} + \vec{BD}$$

As $\vec{BD} = \vec{AE} = \mathbf{q}$, this gives:

$$\vec{AD} = \mathbf{p} + \mathbf{q}$$

c) $\vec{AF} = \vec{AE} + \vec{EF} = \mathbf{q} + \vec{EF}$

But $\vec{EF} = \vec{BA} = -\mathbf{p}$. So, you have:

$$\vec{AF} = \mathbf{q} - \mathbf{p}$$

d) $\vec{EC} = \vec{EA} + \vec{AC} = -\mathbf{q} + 2\mathbf{p}$

M1

Example 12

ABCD is a parallelogram. E is the mid-point of AC.
Vector $\vec{AB} = \mathbf{p}$ and vector $\vec{AD} = \mathbf{q}$. Find a) $\vec{BE}$ b) $\vec{BD}$.
What can be deduced from the result?

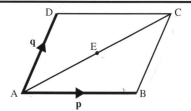

a) First notice that:

$$\vec{AC} = \vec{AB} + \vec{BC} = \mathbf{p} + \mathbf{q}$$

and that:

$$\vec{AE} = \tfrac{1}{2}\vec{AC} = \tfrac{1}{2}(\mathbf{p} + \mathbf{q})$$

Therefore, you have:

$$\vec{BE} = \vec{BA} + \vec{AE}$$
$$= -\mathbf{p} + \tfrac{1}{2}(\mathbf{p} + \mathbf{q})$$
$$= \tfrac{1}{2}(\mathbf{q} - \mathbf{p})$$

b) $\vec{BD} = \vec{BC} + \vec{CD} = \mathbf{q} - \mathbf{p}$

You can see from this that $\vec{BE} = \tfrac{1}{2}\vec{BD}$. This means that BE is half the length of BD and BED is a straight line. That is, E is the mid-point of BD. This proves that the diagonals of a parallelogram bisect each other.

> Many standard geometrical theorems can be proved in this way by vector methods.

Example 13

An expedition travels 10 km on a bearing of 080° and then 8 km on a bearing of 045°. What is the expedition's final position in relation to its starting point?

The stages of the journey are shown in the diagram.

The resultant displacement is the vector $\vec{AC}$, which is the hypotenuse of the right-angled triangle AEC.

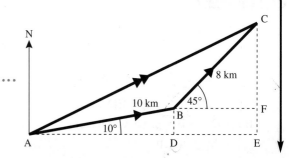

You have:

$$AE = AD + DE$$

But $AD = 10 \cos 10°$ from triangle ADB, and
$DE = BF = 8 \cos 45°$ from triangle BFC. So,
you get:

$$AE = 10 \cos 10° + 8 \cos 45° = 15.5 \text{ km}$$

Similarly, $EC = EF + FC$:

$$EC = 10 \sin 10° + 8 \sin 45° = 7.39 \text{ km}$$

So, you have:

$$AC = \sqrt{AE^2 + EC^2}$$
$$= \sqrt{(15.5)^2 + (7.39)^2} = 17.17 \text{ km}$$

The bearing of AC is $090° - C\hat{A}E$, where:

$$\tan C\hat{A}E = \frac{7.39}{15.5} = 0.476\,77$$

which gives $C\hat{A}E = 25.5°$.

So, $\overrightarrow{AC}$ is a displacement of 17.2 km on a bearing of 064.5°.

M1

In the examples given so far, the vectors have all been displacements.
In the next example, velocities are introduced, but vector diagrams
can still be drawn, in which the vectors appear as displacements.

Example 14

A swimmer, who can swim at 0.8 m s^{-1} in still water, wishes to
cross a river flowing at 0.5 m s^{-1}.

a) If she aims straight across the river, what will be her actual
   velocity?

b) If she wishes to travel straight across, in what direction should
   she aim and what will be her actual speed?

· ·

The simplifying assumption needs to be made that the water flows
at a uniform speed at all points on the crossing. Then the velocities
can be represented by the vector diagrams shown.

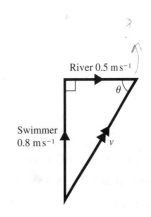

River 0.5 m s^{-1}

Swimmer
0.8 m s^{-1}

a) The swimmer's actual speed is v. So, you have:

$$v = \sqrt{0.8^2 + 0.5^2} = 0.943 \text{ m s}^{-1}$$

Her direction θ is given by:

$$\tan \theta = \frac{0.8}{0.5} \quad \Rightarrow \quad \theta = 58.0°$$

So, the swimmer travels at 0.943 m s^{-1} at an angle of 58° to the
direction of the river.

b) The direction of the swimmer's aim is given by:

$$\cos \phi = \frac{0.5}{0.8} \quad \Rightarrow \quad \phi = 51.3°$$

Her actual speed is given by:

$$u = \sqrt{0.8^2 - 0.5^2} = 0.624 \text{ m s}^{-1}$$

So, she should aim upstream at 51.3° to the bank. She will then travel straight across the river at 0.624 m s^{-1}.

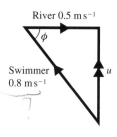

River 0.5 m s^{-1}

Swimmer 0.8 m s^{-1}

u

Exercise 2E

M1

1 ABCE is a rectangle. CDEF is a rhombus. G is the mid-point of AB. $\vec{AF} = \mathbf{p}$ and $\vec{EB} = \mathbf{q}$.

a) Find in terms of $\mathbf{p}$ and $\mathbf{q}$:

  i) $\vec{AB}$ ii) $\vec{CB}$ iii) $\vec{DB}$

b) Show that $\vec{EB} + \vec{CA} = 2\vec{DF}$.

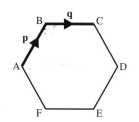

2 The diagram shows a regular hexagon ABCDEF with $\vec{AB} = \mathbf{p}$ and $\vec{BC} = \mathbf{q}$. Find in terms of $\mathbf{p}$ and $\mathbf{q}$:

a) $\vec{AD}$ b) $\vec{AC}$ c) $\vec{CE}$ d) $\vec{BE}$

e) $\vec{EA}$

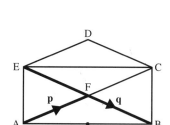

3 The diagram shows a trapezium ABCD with AB parallel to DC and twice as long. E is the mid-point of BC. $\vec{AD} = \mathbf{p}$ and $\vec{DC} = \mathbf{q}$. Find in terms of $\mathbf{p}$ and $\mathbf{q}$:

a) $\vec{AB}$ b) $\vec{AC}$ c) $\vec{CD}$ d) $\vec{DB}$

e) $\vec{AE}$ f) $\vec{ED}$

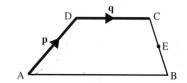

4 Use vector methods to show that the line joining the mid-points of two sides of a triangle is parallel to the third side and half its length.

5 The diagram shows triangle ABC with D, E and F the mid-points of BC, AC and AB respectively. G is the point on AD such that the ratio AG : GD = 2 : 1. Vector $\vec{AB} = \mathbf{p}$ and $\vec{BC} = \mathbf{q}$.

a) Find in terms of $\mathbf{p}$ and $\mathbf{q}$:

  i) $\vec{DB}$ ii) $\vec{DA}$ iii) $\vec{BG}$ iv) $\vec{GE}$

  Explain what your results indicate about the points B, G and E.

b) Prove the equivalent result for points C, G and F.

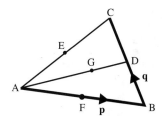

6 ABCD is a quadrilateral. E and F are the mid-points of the diagonals AC and BD respectively.

a) Show that $\vec{AB} + \vec{AD} = 2\vec{AF}$ and $\vec{CB} + \vec{CD} = 2\vec{CF}$.

b) Hence show that $\vec{AB} + \vec{AD} + \vec{CB} + \vec{CD} = 4\vec{EF}$.

7 In each of the following cases, find the magnitude and direction of the resultant of the two given vectors.

a) A displacement of magnitude 3.5 km on a bearing 050° and a displacement of magnitude 5.4 km on a bearing of 128°.

b) A displacement of magnitude 26 km on a bearing of 175° and a displacement of magnitude 18 km on a bearing of 294°.

c) Velocities of 15 km h^{-1} due north and 23 km h^{-1} on a bearing of 253°.

d) Forces of 355 N on a bearing of 320° and 270 N on a bearing of 025°.

8 Two ships, A and B, set out from port O simultaneously. A travels due north at 16 km h^{-1}, B due east at 13 km h^{-1}.

a) The vector $\overrightarrow{AB}$ represents the displacement of B from A. Express this in terms of $\overrightarrow{OA}$ and $\overrightarrow{OB}$.

b) Find the magnitude and direction of $\overrightarrow{AB}$ after i) 1 hour, ii) 3 hours, iii) t hours.

c) The ships' radios have a range of 120 km. For how long will the ships remain in contact?

d) For how long would they remain in contact if B had travelled north-east?

9 A boat which can travel at 5 m s^{-1} in still water is crossing a river 200 m wide. The rate of flow of the river is 2 m s^{-1}, assumed uniform at every point in the river. Points A and B are directly opposite each other across the river.

a) If the boat leaves A and steers towards B, at what speed will it travel and at what point will it reach the opposite bank?

b) If the boat needs to travel towards B, in what direction should it be steered and at what speed will it travel?

10 An aircraft has a speed in still air of 400 km h^{-1}. A wind is blowing from the south at 80 km h^{-1}.

a) The pilot steers the aircraft due east. Find the speed and direction of its actual travel.

b) The pilot wishes the aircraft to travel due east. Find the direction in which the aircraft should be steered and the speed at which it will travel.

11 A ship is being steered due east. A current is flowing from north to south, so that the actual velocity of the ship is 12 km h^{-1} on a bearing of 120°. Find the speed of the current and the still water speed of the ship.

2.7 Components of a vector

To specify vectors, you need a frame of reference. In the previous section, compass directions are used, but more generally the x- and y-axes are preferred.

By convention, **i** and **j** are the unit vectors in the positive x-direction and the positive y-direction respectively. All other vectors can then be formed by combining multiples of **i** and **j**.

For example, in the diagram, the vector $\overrightarrow{OP} = \overrightarrow{OA} + \overrightarrow{AP}$.
But $\overrightarrow{OA} = 3\mathbf{i}$ and $\overrightarrow{AP} = 2\mathbf{j}$, which give:

$$\overrightarrow{OP} = 3\mathbf{i} + 2\mathbf{j}$$

This is called the **x-component** of $\overrightarrow{OP}$ This is called the **y-component** of $\overrightarrow{OP}$

An alternative notation is $\overrightarrow{OP} = \begin{pmatrix} 3 \\ 2 \end{pmatrix}$, which is called a **column vector**.

> **Remember** A unit vector is a vector with a magnitude of 1 unit.

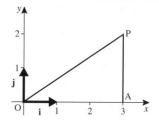

When a vector is given as a magnitude and an angle, it can be converted into component form. This is called **resolving the vector into components**.

M1

In the diagram, the vector $\overrightarrow{OP}$ has magnitude r and direction θ to the positive x-direction.

From the triangle, $x = r \cos \theta$ and $y = r \sin \theta$, which give:

$$\overrightarrow{OP} = r \cos \theta \, \mathbf{i} + r \sin \theta \, \mathbf{j}$$

When you are given the vector in component form:

$$\overrightarrow{OP} = x\mathbf{i} + y\mathbf{j}$$

Its magnitude is given by:

$$r = \sqrt{x^2 + y^2}$$

and its direction by θ, where $\tan \theta = \dfrac{y}{x}$.

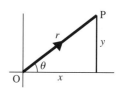

Example 15

Express each of the vectors shown on the left in component form.

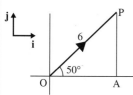

OA = 6 cos 50° = 3.857
AP = 6 sin 50° = 4.596
which give:

$$\overrightarrow{OP} = 3.857\mathbf{i} + 4.596\mathbf{j}$$

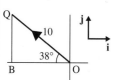

OB = 10 cos 38° = 7.880
BQ = 10 sin 38° = 6.157
which give:

$$\overrightarrow{OQ} = -7.880\mathbf{i} + 6.157\mathbf{j}$$

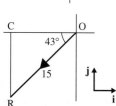

OC = 15 cos 43° = 10.97
CR = 15 sin 43° = 10.23
which give:

$$\overrightarrow{OR} = -10.97\mathbf{i} - 10.23\mathbf{j}$$

Example 16

Find the magnitude and direction of the following vectors:

a) $\mathbf{p} = 2\mathbf{i} + 5\mathbf{j}$ b) $\mathbf{q} = 3\mathbf{i} - 2\mathbf{j}$ c) $\mathbf{r} = -\mathbf{i} - 2\mathbf{j}$

a)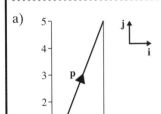

$|\mathbf{p}| = \sqrt{2^2 + 5^2} = 5.385$

$\tan \theta = \dfrac{5}{2} \quad \Rightarrow \quad \theta = 68.2°$

b)

$|\mathbf{q}| = \sqrt{3^2 + (-2)^2} = 3.606$

$\tan \theta = \dfrac{2}{3} \quad \Rightarrow \quad \theta = 33.7°$

c)

$|\mathbf{r}| = \sqrt{(-1)^2 + (-2)^2} = 2.236$

$\tan \theta = 2 \quad \Rightarrow \quad \theta = 63.4°$

> In Example 16, the direction is given as an angle indicated in each diagram. More formally, the direction would be given as a clockwise **rotation**, θ, from the positive x-direction, with $-180° < \theta \leqslant 180°$ and the anticlockwise sense taken as positive. The answers would then be: a) 68.2°, b) −33.7°, c) −116.6°.

M1

Combining vectors in component form

When the vectors $\mathbf{p} = 3\mathbf{i} + \mathbf{j}$ and $\mathbf{q} = 2\mathbf{i} + 3\mathbf{j}$ are added, you can see from the diagram that the resultant is:

$\mathbf{p} + \mathbf{q} = 5\mathbf{i} + 4\mathbf{j}$

So, you have:

$(3\mathbf{i} + \mathbf{j}) + (2\mathbf{i} + 3\mathbf{j}) = 5\mathbf{i} + 4\mathbf{j}$

That is, when adding vectors, the corresponding components are added. It can be generalised to give the following results.

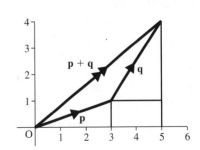

> ✦ $(a\mathbf{i} + b\mathbf{j}) + (c\mathbf{i} + d\mathbf{j}) = (a + c)\mathbf{i} + (b + d)\mathbf{j}$
> ✦ $(a\mathbf{i} + b\mathbf{j}) - (c\mathbf{i} + d\mathbf{j}) = (a - c)\mathbf{i} + (b - d)\mathbf{j}$
> ✦ $k(a\mathbf{i} + b\mathbf{j}) = ka\mathbf{i} + kb\mathbf{j}$ where k is a scalar quantity

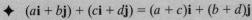

Example 17

Given $\mathbf{p} = 12\mathbf{i} + 5\mathbf{j}$ and $\mathbf{q} = 3\mathbf{i} - 4\mathbf{j}$, find:

a) i) $\mathbf{p} - \mathbf{q}$ ii) $2\mathbf{p} + 3\mathbf{q}$

b) A vector parallel to $\mathbf{p}$ and with magnitude 39

c) Unit vector $\hat{\mathbf{q}}$

···

a) i) $\mathbf{p} - \mathbf{q} = 12\mathbf{i} + 5\mathbf{j} - (3\mathbf{i} - 4\mathbf{j})$
$\qquad\quad = (12 - 3)\mathbf{i} + (5 - (-4))\mathbf{j}$
$\qquad\quad = 9\mathbf{i} + 9\mathbf{j}$

   ii) $2\mathbf{p} + 3\mathbf{q} = 2(12\mathbf{i} + 5\mathbf{j}) + 3(3\mathbf{i} - 4\mathbf{j})$
$\qquad\qquad\quad = (24\mathbf{i} + 10\mathbf{j}) + (9\mathbf{i} - 12\mathbf{j})$
$\qquad\qquad\quad = 33\mathbf{i} - 2\mathbf{j}$

b) $|\mathbf{p}| = \sqrt{12^2 + 5^2} = 13$

A vector $k\mathbf{p}$ is parallel to $\mathbf{p}$ and with k times the magnitude, so the required vector is:

$\qquad 3\mathbf{p} = 36\mathbf{i} + 15\mathbf{j}$

c) $|\mathbf{q}| = \sqrt{3^2 + 4^2} = 5$

$\Rightarrow \quad \hat{\mathbf{q}} = \tfrac{1}{5}\mathbf{q} = 0.6\mathbf{i} - 0.8\mathbf{j}$

Unit vectors

The process used in part c) of Example 17 can be generalised to find the unit vector in the direction of a given vector $\mathbf{a}$:

$$\hat{\mathbf{a}} = \frac{\mathbf{a}}{|\mathbf{a}|}$$

Resultant vectors

Example 18

Find the magnitude and direction of the resultant of the forces shown in the diagram. (N stands for newton, the unit of force, which you will meet on page 49.)

···

To find the resultant, $\mathbf{R}$, each force is expressed in component form and added.

$$\mathbf{R} = \begin{pmatrix} 3 \\ 0 \end{pmatrix} + \begin{pmatrix} 5\cos 74° \\ 5\sin 74° \end{pmatrix} + \begin{pmatrix} -4\cos 20° \\ 4\sin 20° \end{pmatrix} + \begin{pmatrix} 7\cos 55° \\ -7\sin 55° \end{pmatrix} = \begin{pmatrix} 4.63 \\ 0.44 \end{pmatrix}$$

Next, find the magnitude and direction of $\mathbf{R}$.

From the triangle on the right, you have:

$$\mathbf{R} = \sqrt{4.63^2 + 0.44^2} = 4.65 \text{ N}$$

$$\tan\theta = \frac{0.44}{4.63} \quad \Rightarrow \quad \theta = 5.43°$$

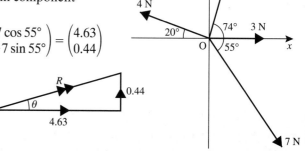

M1

Equality of vectors

Two vectors are equal if and only if their components are equal. That is, if $\mathbf{p} = a\mathbf{i} + b\mathbf{j}$ and $\mathbf{q} = c\mathbf{i} + d\mathbf{j}$, then:

$\mathbf{p} = \mathbf{q}$ implies $a = c$ and $b = d$

Exercise 2F

1 Given vectors $\mathbf{a} = 2\mathbf{i} - \mathbf{j}$, $\mathbf{b} = -2\mathbf{i} + 3\mathbf{j}$ and $\mathbf{c} = 4\mathbf{i} + \mathbf{j}$, calculate each of the following.

a) $\mathbf{a} + \mathbf{b}$ b) $\mathbf{a} - \mathbf{c}$ c) $2\mathbf{b} - \mathbf{a}$

d) $2\mathbf{a} + 3\mathbf{c}$ e) $|\mathbf{a}|$ f) $|\mathbf{b} + \mathbf{c}|$

2 Given vectors $\mathbf{p} = 3\mathbf{i} + u\mathbf{j}$, $\mathbf{q} = v\mathbf{i} - 4\mathbf{j}$ and $\mathbf{r} = 4\mathbf{i} - 6\mathbf{j}$, find each of the following.

a) The values of u and v if $\mathbf{p} - \mathbf{q} = \mathbf{r}$.

b) The value of u if $\mathbf{p}$ and $\mathbf{r}$ are parallel.

M1

3 Given $\mathbf{a} = -3\mathbf{i} + 4\mathbf{j}$, find these.

a) A vector parallel to $\mathbf{a}$ and with magnitude 20.

b) The unit vector $\hat{\mathbf{a}}$ in the direction of $\mathbf{a}$.

4 Express each of the following vectors in the form $x\mathbf{i} + y\mathbf{j}$.

a) 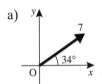   b) 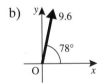   c)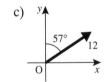

d) 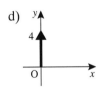   e) 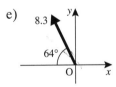   f)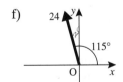

g) 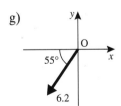   h) 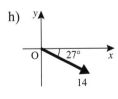   i)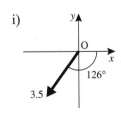

5 Find the magnitude, r, and the direction, θ, of the following vectors, where θ is the anticlockwise rotation from the positive x-direction and $-180° < \theta \leqslant 180°$.

a) $5\mathbf{i} + 2\mathbf{j}$ b) $7\mathbf{i} + 9\mathbf{j}$ c) $-5\mathbf{j}$ d) $-2\mathbf{i} + 3\mathbf{j}$

e) $3\mathbf{i} - 5\mathbf{j}$ f) $-6\mathbf{i} - 5\mathbf{j}$ g) $-2\mathbf{i}$

6 A ship sails from O to A, a distance of 20 km on a bearing of 072°, and then from A to B, a distance of 28 km on a bearing of 024°. Take east to be the x-direction and north the y-direction.

a) Express the displacement vectors $\overrightarrow{OA}$ and $\overrightarrow{AB}$ in component form.

b) Hence find the resultant displacement $\overrightarrow{OB}$ in component form.

c) Find the magnitude and direction of the resultant displacement.

7 Two ships, A and B, leave harbour at O. A travels 35 km on a bearing of 280° and B travels 50 km on a bearing of 030°. Take east to be the x-direction and north the y-direction.

a) Express the displacement vectors $\overrightarrow{OA}$ and $\overrightarrow{OB}$ in component form.

b) Express the vector $\overrightarrow{AB}$ in terms of $\overrightarrow{OA}$ and $\overrightarrow{OB}$, and hence find $\overrightarrow{AB}$ in component form.

c) How far and on what bearing is ship B from ship A?

8 Starting simultaneously from the same spot, O, Alvin and Bernard set out across a field in the fog. Alvin travels with velocity $\mathbf{i} + 2\mathbf{j}\ \text{m s}^{-1}$ and Bernard with velocity $3\mathbf{i} + \mathbf{j}\ \text{m s}^{-1}$. To avoid losing each other, they hold opposite ends of a 90 m string.

a) At what speed is Alvin travelling?

b) Find the directions of travel of the two people and hence the angle between their paths.

c) Find the position vectors $\overrightarrow{OA}$ and $\overrightarrow{OB}$ at time t seconds, and hence the vector $\overrightarrow{AB}$ at that time.

d) Find the value of t for which the string becomes taut.

2.8 Two-dimensional motion with constant acceleration

When an object is moving in two dimensions, its displacement, velocity and acceleration have components in the x and y directions.

The following notation will be used:

Displacement $\quad \mathbf{r} = x\mathbf{i} + y\mathbf{j}$
Initial velocity $\quad \mathbf{u} = u_x\mathbf{i} + u_y\mathbf{j}$
Final velocity $\quad \mathbf{v} = v_x\mathbf{i} + v_y\mathbf{j}$
Acceleration $\quad \mathbf{a} = a_x\mathbf{i} + a_y\mathbf{j}$

Provided a_x and a_y are constant, the motion in each direction will obey the five equations for constant acceleration obtained on pages 20–21.

So, you have:

$$v_x = u_x + a_x t$$
$$v_y = u_y + a_y t$$

These can be combined into the following single-vector equations:

$$v_x\mathbf{i} + v_y\mathbf{j} = (u_x + a_x t)\mathbf{i} + (u_y + a_y t)\mathbf{j}$$
$$v_x\mathbf{i} + v_y\mathbf{j} = (u_x\mathbf{i} + u_y\mathbf{j})\mathbf{i} + (a_x\mathbf{i} + a_y\mathbf{j})t$$

which gives:

$$\mathbf{v} = \mathbf{u} + \mathbf{a}t$$

In the same way, the following can be shown:

$$\mathbf{r} = \tfrac{1}{2}(\mathbf{u} + \mathbf{v})t$$
$$\mathbf{r} = \mathbf{u}t + \tfrac{1}{2}\mathbf{a}t^2$$
$$\mathbf{r} = \mathbf{v}t - \tfrac{1}{2}\mathbf{a}t^2$$

> The fifth equation ($v^2 = u^2 + 2as$) can be written in a vector form but uses techniques beyond the scope of this book. It can still be used separately on components in the x- and y-directions. That is:
>
> $$v_x^2 = u_x^2 + 2a_x x$$
> $$v_y^2 = u_y^2 + 2a_y y$$

M1

Example 19

An object travelling with velocity $(2\mathbf{i} + 15\mathbf{j})$ m s^{-1} underwent an acceleration $(\mathbf{i} - 2\mathbf{j})$ m s^{-2} for a period of 4 seconds.

a) Find its velocity at the end of the 4 seconds.

b) Find the displacement it underwent during the 4 seconds.

c) Find its speed and direction of motion at the end of the 4 seconds.

....

a) You have $\mathbf{u} = (2\mathbf{i} + 15\mathbf{j})$ m s^{-1}, $\mathbf{a} = (\mathbf{i} - 2\mathbf{j})$ m s^{-2} and $t = 4$ s. You need to find $\mathbf{v}$.

Use the formula $\mathbf{v} = \mathbf{u} + \mathbf{a}t$, which gives:

$$\mathbf{v} = (2\mathbf{i} + 15\mathbf{j}) + (\mathbf{i} - 2\mathbf{j}) \times 4$$
$$= 6\mathbf{i} + 7\mathbf{j}$$

So, its velocity at the end of the period was $(6\mathbf{i} + 7\mathbf{j})$ m s^{-1}.

b) To find $\mathbf{r}$, you could use $\mathbf{r} = \tfrac{1}{2}(\mathbf{u} + \mathbf{v})t$, which gives:

$$\mathbf{r} = \tfrac{1}{2}((2\mathbf{i} + 15\mathbf{j}) + (6\mathbf{i} + 7\mathbf{j})) \times 4$$
$$= 16\mathbf{i} + 44\mathbf{j}$$

Alternatively, you could use $\mathbf{r} = \mathbf{u}t + \tfrac{1}{2}\mathbf{a}t^2$, which gives:

$$\mathbf{r} = (2\mathbf{i} + 15\mathbf{j}) \times 4 + \tfrac{1}{2}(\mathbf{i} - 2\mathbf{j}) \times 16$$
$$= 16\mathbf{i} + 44\mathbf{j}$$

So, the object underwent a displacement of $(16\mathbf{i} + 44\mathbf{j})$ m.

c) The speed and direction of motion are the magnitude and direction of the velocity vector, which is:

$$\mathbf{v} = 6\mathbf{i} + 7\mathbf{j}$$

The speed is given by:

$$v = \sqrt{6^2 + 7^2} = 9.22 \text{ m s}^{-1}$$

The direction is given by:

$$\tan\theta = \frac{7}{6} \quad \Rightarrow \quad \theta = 49.4°$$

So, the object was travelling at 9.22 m s^{-1} at 49.4° to the positive x-direction.

Example 20

Two particles, A and B, are moving in a plane in relation to cartesian axes with origin O. Initially, A is at the point $(0, 3)$ and B is at $(2, 1)$. A has a velocity of $(2\mathbf{i} + \mathbf{j})$ m s^{-1} and an acceleration of $(\mathbf{i} - 2\mathbf{j})$ m s^{-2}, and B has a velocity of $(3\mathbf{i} - \mathbf{j})$ m s^{-1} and an acceleration of $2\mathbf{i}$ m s^{-2}. Find the vector $\overrightarrow{AB}$ six seconds later, and hence find the distance between the particles at that time.

For A, you have $\mathbf{u}_A = (2\mathbf{i} + \mathbf{j})$ and $\mathbf{a}_A = (\mathbf{i} - 2\mathbf{j})$.

To find its displacement $\mathbf{r}_A$, use $\mathbf{r} = \mathbf{u}t + \frac{1}{2}\mathbf{a}t^2$, which gives:

$$\mathbf{r}_A = (2\mathbf{i} + \mathbf{j}) \times 6 + \tfrac{1}{2}(\mathbf{i} - 2\mathbf{j}) \times 36$$
$$= 30\mathbf{i} - 30\mathbf{j}$$

As A started at $(0, 3)$, after 6 seconds the vector $\overrightarrow{OA} = 30\mathbf{i} - 27\mathbf{j}$.

Similarly for B, you have $\mathbf{u}_B = (3\mathbf{i} - \mathbf{j})$ and $\mathbf{a}_B = 2\mathbf{i}$.

$$\mathbf{r}_B = (3\mathbf{i} - \mathbf{j}) \times 6 + \tfrac{1}{2}(2\mathbf{i}) \times 36$$
$$= 54\mathbf{i} - 6\mathbf{j}$$

As B started at $(2, 1)$, after 6 seconds the vector $\overrightarrow{OB} = 56\mathbf{i} - 5\mathbf{j}$.

This gives:

$$\overrightarrow{AB} = \overrightarrow{OB} - \overrightarrow{OA} = 26\mathbf{i} + 22\mathbf{j}$$

The distance AB is given by:

$$|\overrightarrow{AB}| = \sqrt{26^2 + 22^2} = 34.1$$

So, the particles are 34.1 m apart.

M1

Exercise 2G

1 A particle is moving in a plane with acceleration $(4\mathbf{i} + 3\mathbf{j})$ m s^{-2}. Its initial velocity is $(2\mathbf{i} - 6\mathbf{j})$ m s^{-1}. After 8 seconds, it has velocity $\mathbf{v}$.

   a) Find $\mathbf{v}$.

   b) Find its speed and direction at this time.

   c) Find the displacement undergone by the particle during this period.

2 A particle is moving in a plane with constant acceleration. Initially, its velocity is $(3\mathbf{i} - 2\mathbf{j})$ m s^{-1} and 6 seconds later it has velocity $(9\mathbf{i} + 4\mathbf{j})$ m s^{-1}.

   a) Find the acceleration of the particle.

   b) Find the displacement undergone by the particle.

   c) Find the distance between the initial and final positions of the particle.

3 A particle is moving with velocity $(6\mathbf{i} + 2\mathbf{j})$ m s^{-1}. It undergoes an acceleration of $(-\mathbf{i} - 7\mathbf{j})$ m s^{-2} for 2 seconds. Show that, at the end of that time, it is travelling in a direction perpendicular to its initial direction, and at twice the speed.

4 A particle is initially travelling with velocity $(4\mathbf{i} + 5\mathbf{j})$ m s^{-1}. It undergoes an acceleration of magnitude 2.5 m s^{-2} in a direction given by the vector $(3\mathbf{i} - 4\mathbf{j})$. Find the velocity and displacement of the particle from its initial position after 4 seconds.

5 A particle P is initially at the point $(2, 6)$ in relation to an origin, O, and is moving with velocity $(3\mathbf{i} + \mathbf{j})$ m s^{-1}. It has constant acceleration $(16\mathbf{i} + 24\mathbf{j})$ m s^{-2}. Show that after 2 seconds it is moving directly away from O, and find its speed at that time.

6 An aircraft is travelling horizontally in an easterly direction at a height of 400 m above level ground and at a speed of 120 m s^{-1}. When it is directly above an observer, M, it releases a package. In relation to the origin O and to x and y directions of east and up respectively, the package has acceleration $(-4\mathbf{j} - 8\mathbf{j})$ m s^{-2}.

   a) P is the position of the package at time t. Find an expression for the vector MP.

   b) Find the length of time the package takes to reach the ground.

   c) Find how far from the observer the package lands.

7 An object is moving in a plane. At time $t = 0$, it is at the origin, O, and moving with velocity $\mathbf{u}$. After 2 seconds, it is at A, where $\overrightarrow{OA} = -2\mathbf{i} - 4\mathbf{j}$. After a further 3 seconds, it is at B, where $\overrightarrow{AB} = 10\mathbf{i} - 40\mathbf{j}$.

   Show that this is consistent with constant acceleration $\mathbf{a}$. Find $\mathbf{a}$ and $\mathbf{u}$.

8 A particle starts at the origin, O. It moves with constant velocity $(2\mathbf{i} + 3\mathbf{j})$ m s^{-1} for 2 seconds. It then accelerates with constant acceleration $(\mathbf{i} - 3\mathbf{j})$ m s^{-2} for 6 seconds, before slowing uniformly to rest in 4 seconds.

   a) Find its displacement during the first stage of the journey.

   b) Find its velocity after the second stage of the journey.

   c) Find its acceleration during the third stage of the journey.

   d) Find its position at the end of the journey.

M1

Summary

You should know how to ...	Check out
1 Identify whether a quantity is a vector or a scalar.	**1** Explain the difference between distance and displacement.
2 Calculate average speed.	**2** John travels at 30 km h^{-1} for 4 hours, then at 60 km h^{-1} for 1 hour. Calculate his average speed.

M1

3 Draw and interpret a displacement–time graph.

3 Anita leaves her house, walks up the road to her friend, Suki, then down the road to her other friend Robin. The graph shows her journey.

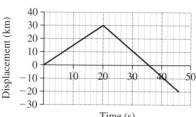

Calculate each of the following.

a) Her total distance travelled.

b) Her total displacement.

c) Her velocity for each stage.

d) Her overall average velocity.

---

4 Draw and interpret a velocity–time graph.

4

The velocity–time graph shows the motion of a particle for one minute. Calculate each of the following.

a) The acceleration in the first 10 s.

b) The total distance travelled.

c) The total displacement.

---

5 Memorise the five formulae for motion with constant acceleration.

5 Write down the five formulae for motion with constant acceleration.

---

6 Use the five formulae for motion with constant acceleration.

6 A body travelling at $8\,\text{m s}^{-1}$ is given a constant acceleration. Five seconds later its velocity is $28\,\text{m s}^{-1}$. Find:

a) its acceleration

b) the distance travelled in the 5 seconds

---

7 Solve problems involving particles moving vertically under gravity.

7 A rock is dropped from the top of a 200 m cliff. How long does it take to reach the bottom?

8 Use vectors geometrically.	**8** In triangle ABC, $\overrightarrow{AB} = \mathbf{p}$, $\overrightarrow{AC} = \mathbf{q}$. Draw these vectors: a) $3\mathbf{p}$ b) $2\mathbf{p} + \mathbf{q}$ c) $\mathbf{p} - 2\mathbf{q}$
9 Manipulate vectors expressed in component form.	**9** $\mathbf{p} = 3\mathbf{i} - 4\mathbf{j}$, $\mathbf{q} = 2\mathbf{i} + 5\mathbf{j}$. Find: a) $4\mathbf{p}$ b) $2\mathbf{p} + 3\mathbf{q}$ c) $\mathbf{p} - 5\mathbf{q}$
10 Resolve a vector into its components.	**10** The vector $\mathbf{p}$ has magnitude 4 and its direction makes an angle of $40°$ with the positive x-direction. Write the vector $\mathbf{p}$ in component form.
11 Find the magnitude and direction of a vector given in component form.	**11** $\mathbf{p} = 6\mathbf{i} - 3\mathbf{j}$. Find a) $|\mathbf{p}|$; b) the direction of $\mathbf{p}$.
12 Memorise the formulae, in vector form, for motion with constant acceleration.	**12** Write down the formulae, in vector form, for motion with constant acceleration.
13 Use the vector equations for motion in two dimensions with constant acceleration.	**13** A particle with velocity $(3\mathbf{i} + \mathbf{j})$ m s^{-1} undergoes acceleration $(\mathbf{i} + 2\mathbf{j})$ m s^{-2} for a period of 3 s. Find the displacement of the particle during this time.

M1

Revision exercise 2

1 A child is playing with a toy aeroplane. The aeroplane is flying with velocity $(6\mathbf{i} + 2\mathbf{j})$ m s^{-1}. A breeze begins to blow with velocity $0.5\mathbf{j}$ m s^{-1} affecting the motion of the aeroplane.

a) Find the magnitude of the resultant velocity of the aeroplane.

b) Find the angle this resultant velocity makes with the unit vector $\mathbf{i}$.

(AQA, 2002)

2 A girl swims across a river. When she swims in still water, she swims at 1.25 m s^{-1}. The river flows parallel to its banks at v m s^{-1}.

The girl aims to swim upstream at an angle θ degrees to the river bank so that her resultant velocity, of magnitude 1 m s^{-1}, is along AB, perpendicular to the river bank.

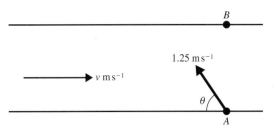

a) Sketch an appropriate triangle of velocities.

b) Find the value of v.

c) Find the value of θ.

(AQA, 2003)

M1

3 A ship moves so that its position vector, in metres, relative to a lighthouse at time t seconds is

$$\mathbf{r} = (80 - 0.4t)\mathbf{i} + (2t - 80)\mathbf{j}$$

where $\mathbf{i}$ and $\mathbf{j}$ are unit vectors directed east and north respectively.

a) Find the distance of the ship from the lighthouse when $t = 60$.

b) Find the times when the ship is i) due north of the lighthouse, ii) north-east of the lighthouse.   (*AQA, 2001*)

4

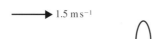

A boy is rowing a boat across a river. When he rows in still water, the boat moves at $2\,\mathrm{m\,s^{-1}}$. The river flows parallel to its banks at $1.5\,\mathrm{m\,s^{-1}}$. The boy aims his boat perpendicular to the banks of the river, but is carried downstream by the river.

a) Sketch an appropriate triangle of velocities.

b) Find the magnitude of the resultant velocity of the boat.

c) Find the angle this resultant velocity makes with the bank of the river, giving your answer to the nearest degree.   (*AQA, 2001*)

5 Two forces, $\mathbf{F}_1 = (3\mathbf{i} + 4\mathbf{j})\mathrm{N}$ and $\mathbf{F}_2 = (6\mathbf{i} - 8\mathbf{j})\mathrm{N}$, act on a particle. The resultant of these two forces is $\mathbf{F}$. The unit vectors $\mathbf{i}$ and $\mathbf{j}$ are perpendicular.

a) Find $\mathbf{F}$.

b) Find the magnitude of $\mathbf{F}$.

c) Find the acute angle between $\mathbf{F}$ and the unit vector $\mathbf{i}$.   (*AQA, 2003*)

6 A stone is released from rest and falls vertically through a distance of 22.5 metres before hitting the ground.

a) Calculate the velocity of the stone as it hits the ground.

b) Calculate the time between the stone being released and hitting the ground.

c) Sketch a velocity–time graph to show the motion of the stone while it is falling.

d) State one modelling assumption that you have made in order to answer the question.   (*AQA, 2002*)

7 This question concerns a car and a cyclist that are modelled as particles, that travel in a straight line. The graph shows a velocity–time graph for the car on a short journey, after which it remains at rest. The car travels 20 m at a constant speed.

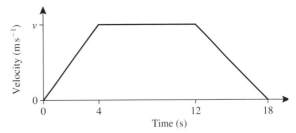

a) Find the acceleration of the car on each stage of the journey and sketch a graph to show how it varies.

b) Find the total distance travelled by the car.

A cyclist is next to the car at $t = 0$, when the car begins to move. The cyclist travels in the same direction as the car at a constant speed of 1.5 m s^{-1}.

c) Does the car or the cyclist travel the greater distance in the first 4 seconds? Find the time when they have travelled the same distance.

d) Would you encounter any difficulties if you do not model the car and the cyclist as particles?   *(AQA, 2000)*

8 A rabbit runs in a horizontal straight line ABC across a field

a) The rabbit runs from rest at A with a constant acceleration of 0.8 m s^{-2} and reaches B after 3 seconds. Find its speed at B.

b) The rabbit then runs from B with constant speed and reaches C after a further 4 seconds. Sketch a velocity–time graph of the motion of the rabbit as it runs from A to C.

c) Find the average speed of the rabbit as it runs from A to C.   *(AQA, 2003)*

9 The velocity–time graphs show the motion of a car and a bicycle as they travel along a straight horizontal road. When $t = 0$, the car and bicycle pass a traffic light on the road. At the traffic light, the bicycle is travelling at a constant velocity of 5 m s^{-1}, but the car is travelling at 3 m s^{-1} and accelerating.

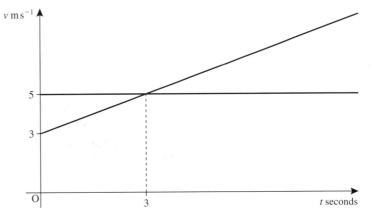

a) i) Explain how the graph indicates that the acceleration of the car is constant.

ii) Find the acceleration of the car.

b) When $t = T$, the car has travelled twice as far from the traffic light as the bicycle. Find the value of T.   *(AQA, 2001)*

M1

10 At time $t = 0$, a boat is travelling due east at a speed of $3\,\mathrm{m\,s^{-1}}$.
The unit vectors **i** and **j** are directed east and north respectively.

a) Write down the initial velocity of the boat in vector form.

b) The boat has a constant acceleration of $(0.1\mathbf{i} + 0.2\mathbf{j})\,\mathrm{m\,s^{-2}}$.
Find an expression for the velocity of the boat at time t seconds.

c) When $t = T$, the boat is travelling north-east. Form an equation
that T must satisfy, and solve it to show that $T = 30$.

d) Find the distance of the boat from its initial position when $t = 20$.   *(AQA, 2002)*

11 The velocity–time graph shows the
motion of a particle P moving with
constant acceleration.

At times $t = 2$ and $t = 5$, P has
velocities $3U$ and $5U$ respectively.

a) i) Find, in terms of U, the
acceleration of P.

ii) Find, in terms of U, the
distance travelled by P between
the times $t = 2$ and $t = 5$.

b) When $t = 5$, the motion of P
changes and subsequently P moves
with constant retardation. The
particle P comes to rest after travelling
a **further** 20 metres in the next 4 seconds.

Find the value of U.

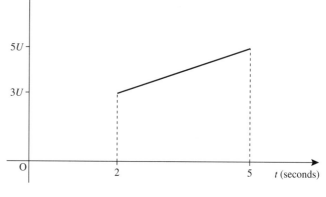

(AQA, 2003)

12 A particle moves in the horizontal plane that contains the
perpendicular unit vectors **i** and **j**. Initially, it is at the origin and
has velocity $18\mathbf{i}\,\mathrm{m\,s^{-1}}$. After accelerating for 10 seconds, its
velocity is $(30\mathbf{i} + 8\mathbf{j})\,\mathrm{m\,s^{-1}}$. Assume that the acceleration of the
particle is constant.

a) Find the acceleration of the particle.

b) Find the position vector of the particle when its velocity is
$(36\mathbf{i} + 12\mathbf{j})\,\mathrm{m\,s^{-1}}$.   *(AQA, 2001)*

13 A student attempts to model the motion of a bungee jumper.
He draws the velocity–time graph shown below.

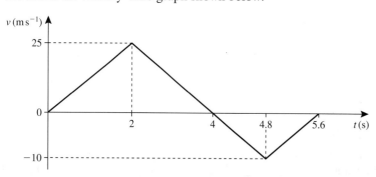

a) State the two non-zero times at which the velocity of the bungee jumper is zero.

b) Find the distance that the bungee jumper falls during the first 4 seconds.

c) Find the total distance travelled by the bungee jumper during the 5.6 seconds illustrated on the graph.

d) Find the acceleration of the bungee jumper during the first 2 seconds and hence state one problem with the proposed model.

e) Make one other criticism of the model, explaining its significance.   (*AQA, 2002*)

14 A particle is initially at the origin. The particle has a constant acceleration of $(2\mathbf{i} - 3\mathbf{j})$ m s^{-2}. Two seconds after it has left the origin, the velocity of the particle is $(2\mathbf{i} + 14\mathbf{j})$ m s^{-1}. The unit vectors $\mathbf{i}$ and $\mathbf{j}$ are perpendicular.

a) Show that the initial velocity of the particle is $(-2\mathbf{i} + 20\mathbf{j})$ m s^{-1}.

b) Find the distance of the particle from the origin after 3 seconds.

c) The speed of the particle is 10 m s^{-1} for the first time T seconds after it has left the origin. Find T.   (*AQA, 2003*)

M1

15 A boat moves with a constant acceleration of $(0.2\mathbf{i} + 0.1\mathbf{j})$ m s^{-2}, where the unit vectors $\mathbf{i}$ and $\mathbf{j}$ are directed east and north respectively. Time t is measured in seconds.

At time $t = 10$, the boat is at the point A, which has position vector $(30\mathbf{i} - 35\mathbf{j})$ metres.
At time $t = 20$, the boat is at the point B, which has position vector $(70\mathbf{i} - 40\mathbf{j})$ metres.

a) Find the vector $\overrightarrow{AB}$.

b) Find the velocity of the boat when $t = 10$.

c) Using your answer to part b), find the velocity of the boat when $t = 0$.

d) Find the position vector of the boat when $t = 0$.   (*AQA, 2003*)

3 Statics and forces

This chapter will show you how to

+ Identify different types of force
+ Draw diagrams showing all the forces acting on a body
+ Resolve forces
+ Calculate unknown forces for a system in equilibrium
+ Model the effects of friction

Before you start

You should know how to ...	Check in
1 Use appropriate modelling.	**1** A brick is suspended from a horizontal beam by means of two strings attached to different points on the beam. What modelling assumptions should be made?
2 Use trigonometry in a right-angled triangle.	**2** In the triangle ABC, find: a) AC b) BC.
3 Solve simultaneous equations.	**3** Solve: $3x + 4y = 24$ $5x - 2y = 14$
4 Solve three equations with three unknowns by repeated elimination.	**4** Find F, P and R, given that: $F = 0.2R$ $P \sin 20° + R = 20$ $P \cos 20° = F$
5 Manipulate inequalities.	**5** Find x when: a) $2x - 3 \geqslant 11$ b) $4 - x \leqslant 6$

Everyone has an intuitive idea of what is meant by force. When you cycle, you are aware of the force of air resistance. When you lift an object, you are aware of the force of gravity. When you water-ski, you are subject to the tension force of the towline. When you kneel down for any length of time, you suffer from the reaction force of the floor pressing on your knees.

Force is a vector quantity, because its effect is dependent on its magnitude and its direction. Additionally, the effect of a force varies depending on the point at which it is applied – its **line of action**. In this chapter, objects are modelled as masses concentrated at a single point, so rotational effects are not involved.

> For example, attaching a crane hook to the end of a girder or to its middle gives different results on lifting. In the first case, the force would have a rotational effect.

As far as the motion of an object is concerned, the important thing is the total effect – the **resultant** – of the forces acting on it. In this section, only those situations are considered where the resultant force is zero and so does not affect the motion of the object. In this case, the object is in **equilibrium**. That is, the forces acting on it are in equilibrium.

The SI unit of force is the **newton** (N). This is defined as the force needed to accelerate an object of mass 1 kg with an acceleration of $1\,\mathrm{m\,s^{-2}}$. (This is explored more fully in Chapter 4, pages 77–84.)

3.1 The force of gravity

It is important that you are clear about the difference between **mass** and **weight**.

The mass of an object, measured in kilograms, depends only on the amount of matter forming the object. The mass of an object is the **same** wherever it is placed in the universe.

> A kilogram was originally defined as the mass of 1 litre of pure water.

M1

When an object is placed near another object, they are each subject to a force arising from their gravitational attraction for each other. The size of this force depends on their masses and the distance between their centres of mass. You will be aware that an object at or near the surface of the Earth is subject to the force of gravity acting downwards . This force is the weight of the object, measured in newtons. The weight of an object would be **different** if the object were placed on the Moon, although its mass would be unchanged.

> The Earth is acted upon by an equal force acting upwards.

In Newton's model of the universe, the force in newtons between two objects of masses m_1 and m_2 (in kilograms) separated by a distance d metres is given by:

$$F = \frac{Gm_1m_2}{d^2}$$

G is called the **gravitational constant**, which is $6.67 \times 10^{-11}\,\mathrm{N\,m^2\,kg^{-2}}$.

> This relationship, called Newton's Law of Gravitation, is not required for M1. It is included here to show you why weight = 9.8 × mass of an object near the Earth's surface.

The mass of the Earth is $5.98 \times 10^{24}\,\mathrm{kg}$. For a small object of mass m kg near the surface of the Earth, the distance d between its centre and the Earth's centre is the radius of the Earth, which is approximately 6.37×10^6 m. This gives the force acting on the object as

$$F = \frac{(6.67 \times 10^{-11}) \times (5.98 \times 10^{24})m}{(6.37 \times 10^6)^2}$$

$$= 9.8\,m \text{ newtons}$$

This means that an object of mass m kg near the surface of the Earth is subject to a constant downward force – its weight – of $9.8\,m$ N. As you will see on page 82, the 9.8 is the **acceleration due to gravity** and is represented by g:

$$g \approx 9.8\,\mathrm{m\,s^{-2}}$$

For most purposes, g is taken to be constant everywhere at or near the Earth's surface. This assumes that the Earth can be thought of as a sphere which is uniformly dense or is at least formed of concentric shells of uniform density.

3.2 Types of force

In addition to weight, there are other forces which may act on objects. The four considered here are **tension**, **thrust**, **normal reaction** and **friction**.

Tension forces

When a string is pulled, it will exert a tension force opposing the pull. Assuming that the string is **light** (that is, its mass is negligible compared with the rest of the system), the tension force will be the **same** throughout the string.

The woman is holding an object of mass 3 kg suspended on a light string.

The tension, T, exerts an upward force on the object and an equal downward force on the woman's hand.

When the object is stationary, the tension must balance the weight, so:

$$T = 3g$$

Similarly, the woman's hand is stationary, so she must be exerting an upward force of $3g$ N to balance the downward pull of the tension in the string.

The tension in a light string passing over a pulley can still be taken as constant throughout its length provided the pulley is **smooth**. That is, any friction forces are so small as to be negligible.

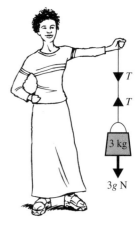

M1

Example 1

Two boxes, A and B, each of mass 40 kg, are connected by a light rope. A second rope is attached to B and passes over a smooth pulley. The other end of this rope is then fixed to the ground at C. What forces act on a) box A, b) box B and c) the ground at C?

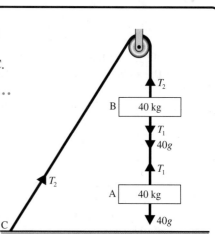

a) The forces on box A are its weight, $40g$ N, acting downwards, and the tension T_1, acting upwards. The box is stationary, so:

$$T_1 = 40g \text{ N}$$

b) The forces on box B are its weight, $40g$ N, the tension T_1 acting downwards, and the tension T_2 acting upwards. The box is stationary, so:

$$T_2 = T_1 + 40g = 80g \text{ N}$$

c) The pulley is smooth, so the tension is the same throughout the rope joining box B to C. This means that the rope is pulling at the ground with a force of $80g$ N.

Forces in rods: thrust

In the example where the woman was supporting the 3 kg mass, the string could have been replaced by a light rod without altering the forces involved. Rods can, therefore, also be under tension. However, unlike strings, it makes sense to push the end of a rod. The rod will exert an opposing push, called a **thrust** or **compression**. Like tension, thrust is the **same** throughout a light rod.

The diagram shows a bird table supported by a light, vertical rod.

The rod exerts an upward thrust force, T, on the table, which is equal to the downward force supplied by the weight, W, of the table and the bird.

At the bottom of the rod, there is an equal downward thrust force exerted on the ground by the rod. This will be countered by an equal force exerted by the ground on the rod.

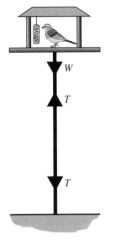

M1

Contact forces

There are two types of force which occur as a result of contact between objects: **normal reaction** and **friction.**

Normal reaction
Consider a cup resting on a table. As it is in equilibrium, the downward force of its weight, W, must be balanced by an upward force, R, exerted by the table.

Similarly, if a trap door of weight W is open and resting on a support, as shown, the support must provide a force R to help keep the trap door in equilibrium. This force is at right angles to the trap door. (There will also be a force at the hinge, but this is not a contact force as the door is fastened to the hinge.)

In each case, the reaction force is at right angles to (normal to) the plane of contact, and so such a force is called a normal reaction.

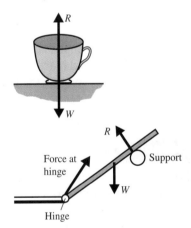

Friction
When you try to drag an object along the ground and start by pulling gently on the rope, the object will not move. The force you are exerting is being balanced by the force of friction. When you gradually increase the pulling force, P, the friction force, F, increases to match it until it reaches its maximum. If you pull harder than this, the object will move, although there will still be a friction force resisting its motion.

Friction **always** acts in a direction opposite to that in which the object is moving or tending to move.

The maximum friction depends on the nature of the surfaces in contact and the normal reaction between these surfaces. In some cases, the friction force is small enough to be ignored. This is said to be a **smooth** contact.

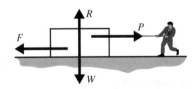

Modelling friction is covered in Examples 2 to 4 on pages 52–53, on pages 63–70, in Examples 7 to 10 on pages 83–84, and in Examples 6 to 8 on pages 104–106.

Resistive forces also occur when an object moves through the air or through a liquid. In some situations, these forces are small enough to be ignored in a model. In other situations, they must be taken into account. For example, in modelling the motion of a ball-bearing falling a short distance in air, you could probably safely ignore air resistance, but for a sheet of paper falling through air or a ball-bearing falling in a tank of oil, you would have to take account of the resistance. Like contact friction, the resistance of air or a liquid always acts to oppose the motion of the object.

3.3 Drawing diagrams

When solving problems in mechanics, it is vital that you draw clear, careful diagrams of a good size, and mark in all the forces involved in your model, together with relevant lengths and angles. This will help you to analyse the problem and to explain clearly the steps in your solution.

M1

Example 2

A large box of mass m kg is being towed up a rough slope inclined at 30° to the horizontal using a rope at 20° to the slope. Draw a diagram to show the forces acting on the box.

The forces acting on the box are its weight, mg, the tension, T, in the rope, the normal reaction, R, and the friction, F, which acts down the slope to oppose the motion.

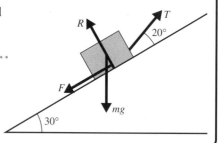

Example 3

The same box is now allowed to slide down the slope controlled by the rope. Draw the forces in this situation.

The only difference in this situation is that the box is moving down the slope and so the friction force acts up the slope to oppose it.

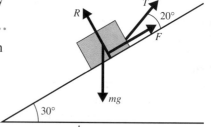

Example 4

A car of mass M kg is towing a trailer of mass m kg on a light rigid towbar. There are resistances to motion F_C and F_T on the car and trailer respectively. Draw diagrams to show the forces acting on the car and on the trailer:

a) When the car exerts a driving force P N.

b) When the car exerts a braking force B N.

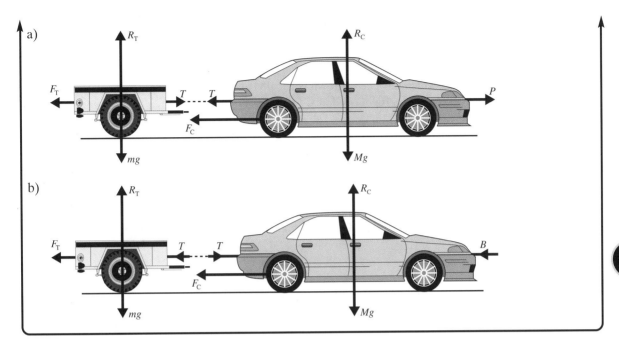

Note the following factors in Example 4.

◆ In case a), the towbar is in tension. In case b), it is under thrust.

◆ The tension/thrust forces are usually shown only when the car and the trailer are considered separately. But when the car and the trailer are treated as a single system, the tension/thrust forces are **internal forces**, which are not shown.

◆ Strictly, the upward reaction on the car consists of four reactions, one at each wheel. But they are usually shown as a single combined reaction unless the force on each wheel is being examined.

◆ Strictly, the forward driving force, P, is actually the friction between the driven wheels and the ground, which acts in a forward direction to prevent the wheels from spinning. However, for most purposes, P can be shown as generalised forward driving force.

Exercise 3A

1 Copy each of the following diagrams and mark in the forces indicated.

a) The forces acting on this brick which is sliding down a rough inclined plank.

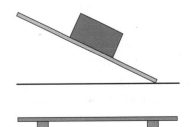

b) The forces on this shelf, supported symmetrically on two brackets.

c) The forces on the shelf, supported by one bracket and an inclined wire.

d) The forces on this ball, which has been thrown vertically, at A (on the way up), at B (top of its flight) and at C (on the way down).

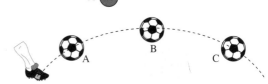

e) The forces on this football at A, B and C.

f) The forces on this ladder which is resting on rough horizontal ground and against a rough vertical wall.

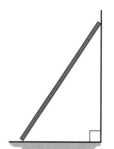

2 A block A, of mass M_A, rests on a rough horizontal table. It is connected to a second block B, of mass M_B, by a light string. The string passes over a smooth pulley at the edge of the table and B hangs suspended.
   a) Draw a diagram to show the forces acting on each of the blocks.
   b) Assuming that the system remains at rest, state the tension in the string and the friction force acting on the block A.

3 A man of mass m stands in a lift of mass M which is supported by a cable. Draw separate diagrams to show the forces acting a) on the lift and b) on the man.

4 A uniform ladder of mass m and length $4a$ rests with one end on rough horizontal ground. The ladder leans against a rough garden wall so that one quarter of its length protrudes above the wall. Draw a diagram to show the forces acting on the ladder.

5 A glass rod rests in a smooth hemispherical bowl so that part of the rod extends beyond the rim of the bowl. Draw a diagram to show the forces acting on the rod.

6 A small object of mass m is suspended by a light string, the other end of which is tied to a fixed support A. The object moves in a horizontal circle below A (this arrangement is known as a conical pendulum). Draw a diagram to show the forces acting on the object.

7 In this diagram, the pulleys are smooth, the strings light and inextensible.

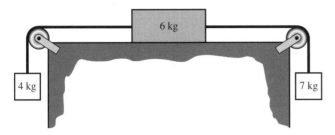

Draw a diagram to show the forces on the 6 kg mass, and calculate the friction force acting on it if the system is at rest.

M1

8 The diagram shows a light rod AB hinged to a vertical wall at A, and a light string BC attached to the rod at B and the wall at C. A mass of 2 kg is suspended from B. Draw a diagram to show the forces acting at the point B.

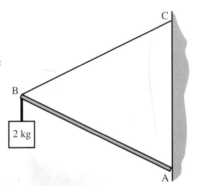

3.4 Forces at a point: modelling by vectors

Force is a vector quantity, having both magnitude and direction. So, vector techniques can be used to study systems of forces acting at a single point.

Example 5

The diagram shows four horizontal dog leads OA, OB, OC and OD, each tied to the same post at O. The dogs are pulling on the leads with forces as shown. Find their combined effect.

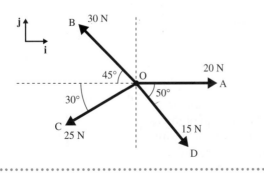

The four forces are equivalent to a single force, the **resultant**. The magnitude and direction of the resultant can be found from a scale drawing or by calculation.

Scale drawing

The forces are represented by the displacements $\vec{PQ}$, $\vec{QR}$, $\vec{RS}$ and $\vec{ST}$ in the drawing. The resultant force is then represented by the displacement $\vec{PT}$.

> If you try to do the scale drawing for yourself, you should obviously use a larger scale to achieve a reasonable degree of accuracy.

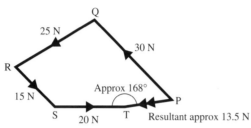

Scale: 1mm ≡ 1 N

When the diagram is drawn to scale, you will find by measurement that the resultant force is approximately 13.5 N, acting at approximately −168° to the direction OA in the first diagram.

> Scale-drawing methods are not a requirement of the M1 specification and will **not** be accepted as solutions in the examination.

Calculation

Taking the vectors **i** and **j** to be in the directions shown in the first diagram, each of the forces can be expressed in component form and added directly.

If **R** is the resultant force, you have:

$$\mathbf{R} = (20\mathbf{i}) + (-30\cos 45°\,\mathbf{i} + 30\sin 45°\,\mathbf{j})$$
$$+ (-25\cos 30°\,\mathbf{i} - 25\sin 30°\,\mathbf{j})$$
$$+ (15\cos 50°\,\mathbf{i} - 15\sin 50°\,\mathbf{j})$$
$$= -13.22\mathbf{i} - 2.78\mathbf{j}$$

The magnitude of **R** is then given by:

$$|\mathbf{R}| = \sqrt{13.22^2 + 2.78^2}$$
$$= 13.51 \text{ N}$$

and its direction is given by θ, where:

$$\tan\theta = \frac{2.78}{13.22} \quad \Rightarrow \quad \theta = 11.86°$$

Forces in equilibrium

When a system of forces acting at a single point has a resultant of zero, the forces are said to be in **equilibrium**. The system of forces in Example 5 would be in equilibrium if you added a fifth force with magnitude 13.51 N acting at 11.86° to OA. This additional force is sometimes referred to as the **equilibrant** for the system.

When a system of forces is in equilibrium, the polygon produced when making a scale drawing is closed, because the total effect of the displacements would be to return to the starting point. This is called a **polygon of forces**.

Consider an object of mass 12 kg suspended by two light, inextensible strings AB and BC. The task is to calculate the tensions in the two strings.

> Although it is rare to use a scale drawing to solve a problem, knowing that the forces can be represented by a closed polygon can be useful, especially in cases involving three forces acting at a point, when you have a **triangle of forces**.

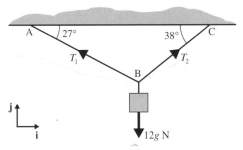

M1

Method 1: resolving forces
The forces are expressed in component form, taking the **i**- and **j**-directions horizontally and vertically, as shown in the diagram above. The resultant force is zero, so you have:

$$(-T_1 \cos 27° \, \mathbf{i} + T_1 \sin 27° \, \mathbf{j}) + (T_2 \cos 38° \, \mathbf{i} + T_2 \sin 38° \, \mathbf{j})$$
$$+ (-12g\mathbf{j}) = \mathbf{0}$$
$$\Rightarrow \quad (-T_1 \cos 27° + T_2 \cos 38°)\mathbf{i}$$
$$+ (T_1 \sin 27° + T_2 \sin 38° - 12g)\mathbf{j} = \mathbf{0}$$

Equating the **i**-component and the **j**-component to zero, you obtain:

$$-T_1 \cos 27° + \cos 38° = 0 \quad \text{and} \quad T_1 \sin 27° + T_2 \sin 38° - 12g = 0$$

Now write the above as simultaneous equations:

$$-0.891T_1 + 0.788T_2 = 0 \qquad \qquad [1]$$
$$0.454T_1 + 0.616T_2 = 117.6 \qquad \qquad [2]$$

Solving equations [1] and [2] gives $T_1 = 102$ N and $T_2 = 116$ N (to the nearest 1 N).

In this method, the vector equation is often omitted and the two component equations are written down directly. You need to indicate where the equations have come from, so the solution would look like this:

> Resolving horizontally gives: $\quad -T_1 \cos 27° + T_2 \cos 38° = 0$
> Resolving vertically gives: $\qquad -T_1 \sin 27° + T_2 \sin 38° - 12g = 0$

followed by solving the simultaneous equations, as before.

Method 2: triangles of forces
For those of you who have studied the sine rule, a solution is available using the triangle of forces.

The three forces are in equilibrium and so they can be represented by the side of a triangle, as shown.

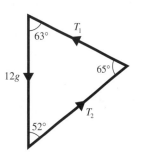

Using the sine rule, you get:

$$\frac{T_1}{\sin 52°} = \frac{T_2}{\sin 63°} = \frac{12g}{\sin 65°}$$

which gives:

$$T_1 = \frac{12g \sin 52°}{\sin 65°} = 102 \text{ N} \quad \text{(to the nearest 1 N)}$$

$$T_2 = \frac{12g \sin 63°}{\sin 65°} = 116 \text{ N} \quad \text{(to the nearest 1 N)}$$

Lami's theorem

In Method 2, it is possible to write down equations equivalent to those obtained from the sine rule without drawing the triangle.

M1

In your GCSE mathematics course, you may have met the fact that $\sin \theta = \sin (180° - \theta)$. Therefore, it follows that:

$$\frac{T_1}{\sin 52°} = \frac{T_2}{\sin 63°} = \frac{12g}{\sin 65°}$$

is equivalent to:

$$\frac{T_1}{\sin 128°} = \frac{T_2}{\sin 117°} = \frac{12g}{\sin 115°}$$

These angles are those opposite the appropriate forces, as shown in the diagram.

This rule can be stated in general:

> For any set of three concurrent forces P, Q, R in equilibrium as shown:
>
> $$\frac{P}{\sin \alpha} = \frac{Q}{\sin \beta} = \frac{R}{\sin \gamma}$$

This is known as **Lami's theorem**.

> Knowledge of Lami's theorem is not required for the M1 specification, but it will be accepted as a method of solution in the examination.

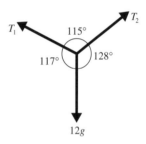

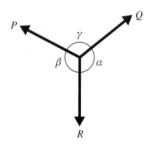

Example 6

A block of mass 4 kg lies at rest on a smooth plane, which is inclined at 25° to the horizontal. It is kept in place by a light string which is angled at 15° to the plane. Find the tension, P, in the string and the normal reaction, R, of the plane on the block.

··

There are three ways to solve this problem: by resolving forces, by solving a triangle of forces, or by applying Lami's theorem.

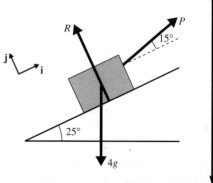

Resolving the forces

Take the **i**- and **j**-directions parallel to and perpendicular to the plane, as shown in the diagram on page 58.

Resolving in the **i**-direction: $P \cos 15° - 4g \sin 25° = 0$ [1]

Resolving in the **j**-direction: $P \sin 15° + R - 4g \cos 25° = 0$

[2]

From equation [1], you obtain:

$$P = \frac{4g \sin 25°}{\cos 15°} = 17.15 \text{ N}$$

Substituting $P = 17.15$ N in equation [2], you have:

$$17.15 \sin 15° + R - 4g \cos 25° = 0$$

which gives:

$$R = 31.09 \text{ N}$$

M1

Triangle of forces

The forces are in equilibrium and can therefore be represented by the sides of a triangle, as shown.

Using the sine rule, you obtain:

$$\frac{P}{\sin 25°} = \frac{R}{\sin 50°} = \frac{4g}{\sin 105°}$$

which gives:

$$P = \frac{4g \sin 25°}{\sin 105°} = 17.15 \text{ N} \quad \text{and} \quad R = \frac{4g \sin 50°}{\sin 105°} = 31.09 \text{ N}$$

Lami's theorem

The angles between the forces are as shown.

Then, according to Lami's theorem, you have:

$$\frac{P}{\sin 155°} = \frac{R}{\sin 130°} = \frac{4g}{\sin 75°}$$

which gives:

$$P = \frac{4g \sin 155°}{\sin 75°} = 17.15 \text{ N}$$

$$R = \frac{4g \sin 130°}{\sin 75°} = 31.09 \text{ N}$$

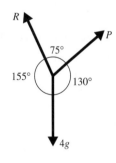

More than three forces

Although any set of concurrent forces in equilibrium can be represented by the sides of a closed polygon, when four or more forces are involved the only practical method of solution is to resolve the forces.

Example 7

An object A of weight W is suspended by light strings AB and AC attached to points B and C. BC is horizontal and of length 5 m. AB and AC are 4 m and 3 m respectively. A horizontal force, P, is applied to the object so that the tension in AB is twice that in AC. Find, in terms of W, the value of P and the tension in AC.

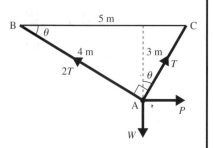

As ABC is a 3-4-5 triangle, $B\hat{A}C$ is 90°. It follows that $\cos \theta = \frac{4}{5}$ and $\sin \theta = \frac{3}{5}$.

For the forces acting on the object:

Resolving vertically gives:
$$T \cos \theta + 2T \sin \theta - W = 0$$
$$\tfrac{4}{5}T + \tfrac{6}{5}T = W$$
$$T = \tfrac{1}{2}W$$

Resolving horizontally gives:
$$P + T \sin \theta - 2T \cos \theta = 0$$
$$P = \tfrac{8}{5}T - \tfrac{3}{5}T = T$$
$$P = \tfrac{1}{2}W$$

Example 8

A smooth ring of mass 3 kg is threaded on a light string 64 cm long. The ends of the string are attached to points A and B on the same level, where AB is 48 cm. A force, P, is applied to the ring so that it rests vertically below B. Find the value of P and the tension in the string.

Since the ring is smooth, the tension is the same throughout the length of the string.

Let BC be x cm, so that AC is $(64 - x)$ cm.

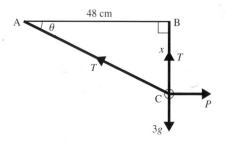

By Pythagoras' theorem:
$$x^2 + 48^2 = (64 - x)^2$$
$$x = 14$$

So, AC = 50 cm and BC = 14 cm, which give:
$$\sin \theta = \tfrac{7}{25} \quad \text{and} \quad \cos \theta = \tfrac{24}{25}$$

For the forces acting on the ring:

Resolving vertically gives:
$$T + T \sin \theta - 3g = 0$$
$$\tfrac{32}{25}T = 3g$$
$$T = 22.97 \, \text{N}$$

Resolving horizontally gives:
$$P - T \cos \theta = 0$$
$$P = \tfrac{24}{25}T = 22.05 \, \text{N}$$

Exercise 3B

1 For each of the following systems of forces, find the resultant
and state the force which would have to be added to the system
to maintain equilibrium.

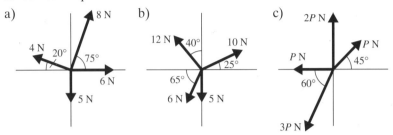

a)   b)   c)

2 Given that each of the following systems of forces is in
equilibrium, find the unknown forces P and Q.

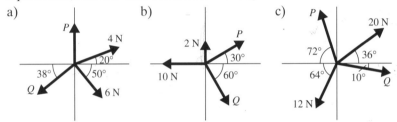

a)   b)   c)

3 Each of the following systems of forces is in equilibrium. For
each one, draw a triangle of forces and from it calculate the
unknown forces and angles.

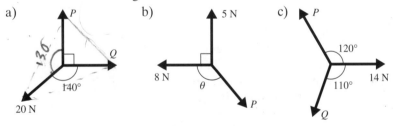

a)   b)   c)

4 Rework the problems in Question **3** using resolution of forces.

5 For each of the following systems of forces in equilibrium, use
Lami's theorem to calculate the unknown forces.

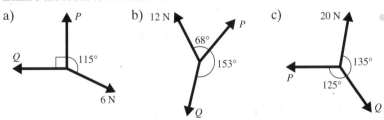

a)   b)   c)

6 A particle of mass 2 kg is suspended by two light strings which
make angles of 30° and 50° with the vertical. Find the tensions in
the strings.

7 A block of mass 9 kg rests on a rough plane inclined at 20° to the horizontal. Find the magnitude of the friction force and the normal reaction acting on the block.

8 A block of mass 20 kg rests on smooth horizontal ground near to a fixed post, to which it is attached by means of a light horizontal rod. The block is being pulled directly away from the post by a force P N inclined at 30° to the horizontal.

   a) Calculate the tension in the rod and the normal reaction between the block and the ground.

   b) Explain what would happen if the value of P exceeded 392 N.

9 The diagram shows a cylinder of mass 8 kg lying at rest on two smooth planes inclined at angles of 40° and 50° to the horizontal. Calculate the reaction forces exerted by the planes on the cylinder.

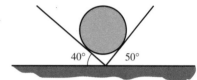

M1

10 A particle of mass 4 kg is suspended from a point A on a vertical wall by means of a light, inextensible string of length 130 cm.

   a) A horizontal force, P, is applied to the particle so that it is held in equilibrium a distance 50 cm from the wall. Find the value of P and the tension in the string.

   b) By drawing a triangle of forces, or otherwise, find the magnitude and direction of the minimum force which would hold the particle in this position, and the tension in the string which would result.

11 Two hooks A and B are fixed to a ceiling, where AB is 2.5 m.

   a) A small object of mass 3 kg is suspended from A and B by two light inextensible strings so that it is 2 m from A and 1.3 m from B. Calculate the tensions in the strings.

   b) The two strings are now replaced by a single string of length 3.3 m which is threaded through a smooth ring attached to the object. A horizontal force, P, is applied to the object so that it rests in the same position in relation to A and B. Calculate the value of P and the tension in the string.

12 A light string of length a is attached to two points A and B on the same level and a distance b apart, where $b < a$. A smooth ring of weight W is threaded on the string and is pulled by a horizontal force, P, so that it rests in equilibrium vertically below B. Show that the tension in the string is

$$\frac{W(a^2 + b^2)}{2a^2}$$

and find the force P.

13 A particle of weight W is attached by a light inextensible string of length a to a point A on a vertical wall. The particle is supported in equilibrium by a light rigid strut of length b attached to a point B on the wall at a distance a vertically below A. Show that the tension in the string is W and find the thrust in the rod.

3.5 Modelling friction

So far, either friction has been assumed to be negligible, or 'frictional resistance forces' have been mentioned without discussing how they might be modelled.

The word 'friction' derives from the Latin *fricare*, which means to rub.

To get a feel for the problems of modelling friction, you should ideally do some practical investigation along the lines suggested in Experiments 1 to 3. Before starting, there are three factors which you should consider.

✦ Friction occurs where you are sliding, or attempting to slide, one surface over another in contact with it.

✦ Friction always tries to prevent movement. The direction of the friction force is always opposite to that in which the object is moving or would move if there were no friction.

✦ Friction is a passive force. That is, it happens as a response to an attempt to slide surfaces, one over the other. A block placed on a table has no friction force acting on it unless you try to push it along. When you push gently, the block stays still, meaning that the friction force 'adjusts' to exactly match the applied force, up to a limit beyond which the block starts to move.

M1

The simplest friction situation – a block sliding on a plane surface – will now be investigated.

Experiments

Experiment 1

You need a plank, string, some weights, a pulley and three blocks.

Two of the blocks must be of the same material but their corresponding faces must have different areas. (Or you could have one block with faces of different areas.) The third block should have a markedly different type of surface: for example, you might try sticking sandpaper to it. You need to know the mass of each block.

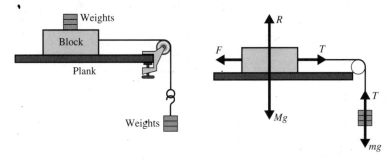

The block is loaded with weights (total mass of block and weights is *M*) and placed on the plank. It is connected to a suspended load, mass *m*, by a string passing over the pulley placed at the end of the plank, as shown.

Assumptions

Two assumptions are made:

✦ The string is light and inextensible.
✦ The pulley is smooth.

The effect of these assumptions is that you can regard the tension, T, as being constant throughout the string.

You will find that, as you increase m, the block initially remains stationary, because the friction force increases to balance the extra load.

However, a point is reached where even a slight increase in the load causes the block to move. At this point, the friction force is at its maximum value, called **limiting friction**.

M1

For this experiment, you should find the value of m corresponding to limiting friction for ten different values of M. (In practice, you may find it easier to fix the value of m and then gradually reduce M until the block is on the point of sliding.)

The contact forces between the block and the plank are the normal reaction, R, and the friction force, F. You find the values of F and R as follows.

Resolving vertically for the suspended mass: $T - mg = 0$ [1]
Resolving horizontally for the block: $F - T = 0$ [2]
Resolving vertically for the block: $R - Mg = 0$ [3]

From equations [1] and [2], you have: $F = mg$

From equation [3], you have: $R = Mg$

Analysis and interpretation

The results should be analysed in a table showing F, R and the ratio F/R. You can also draw a scattergraph of F against R and a line of best fit. This can be done by hand or on a spreadsheet.

The table shows sample results for one run of the experiment. You should repeat it for each of the three blocks, to see the effects of a change of area and a change of surface.

You will probably notice three things.

✦ The values for F/R are approximately the same for different loadings of each particular block. This corresponds to a scattergraph which is convincingly linear and a line of best fit passing through, or near to, the origin (as expected, because a block with zero mass would have zero friction).
✦ The two blocks of the same material but different areas have similar values of F/R.
✦ The value of F/R changes for the block of different material.

> You may find it helpful to download the spreadsheet FRIC1 from the OUP website. Just type in the address:
> http://www.oup.co.uk/secondary/mechanics

Mass on block, M (kg to nearest 0.01)	Suspended mass, m (kg to nearest 0.01)	Reaction, R (newtons)	Friction, F (newtons)	$\dfrac{F}{R}$
0.14	0.03	1.372	0.294	0.214
0.19	0.04	1.862	0.392	0.211
0.24	0.05	2.352	0.490	0.208
0.29	0.06	2.842	0.588	0.207
0.35	0.07	3.430	0.686	0.200
0.41	0.08	4.018	0.784	0.195
0.46	0.09	4.508	0.882	0.196
0.51	0.10	4.998	0.980	0.196
0.56	0.11	5.488	1.078	0.196
0.60	0.12	5.880	1.176	0.200

Mean F/R	0.202

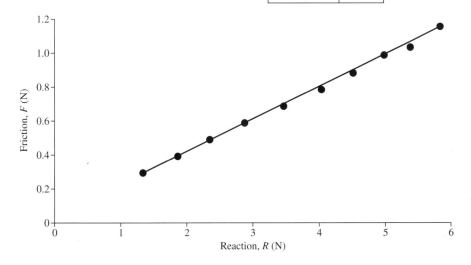

Experiment 2

Experiment 1 suggested that the limiting friction force depends on the reaction between the surfaces. This would seem to make sense – the harder the surfaces are pressed together, the greater the available friction force.

To test this further, you should re-run the experiment with the plank inclined at an angle α to the horizontal, as shown.

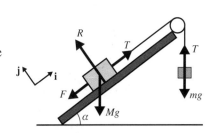

You find the values of F and R as follows.

Resolving vertically for the suspended mass: $T - mg = 0$ [1]

Resolving in the **i**-direction for the block:

$$T - F - Mg \sin \alpha = 0 \qquad [2]$$

Resolving in the **j**-direction for the block:

$$R - Mg \cos \alpha = 0 \qquad [3]$$

From equations [1] and [2], you have: $F = mg - Mg \sin \alpha$

From equation [3], you have: $R = Mg \cos \alpha$

Analysis and interpretation

You should tabulate the values of F, R and F/R as before, and draw a scattergraph.

The table shows sample results for this experiment, using $\alpha = 30°$.

A second spreadsheet, FRIC2, can be downloaded from the OUP website for this purpose. Just type in the address:
http://www.oup.co.uk/secondary/mechanics

M1

Mass on block, M (kg to nearest 0.01)	Suspended mass, m (kg to nearest 0.01)	Reaction, R (newtons)	Friction, F (newtons)	$\dfrac{F}{R}$
0.11	0.07	0.934	0.147	0.157
0.12	0.08	1.018	0.196	0.192
0.14	0.09	1.188	0.196	0.165
0.15	0.10	1.273	0.245	0.192
0.16	0.11	1.358	0.294	0.217
0.18	0.12	1.528	0.294	0.192
0.20	0.13	1.697	0.294	0.173
0.21	0.14	1.782	0.343	0.192
0.23	0.15	1.952	0.343	0.176
0.24	0.16	2.037	0.392	0.192

Mean F/R	0.185

You should find that the value F/R again remains approximately constant for a given pair of surfaces, and that this constant value is similar to that obtained in Experiment 1.

Coefficient of friction

The results of Experiments 1 and 2 suggest the following.

✦   As the force on the block increases, the friction force increases to counteract it exactly, up to a maximum called the **limiting friction**. The system is then said to be in **limiting equilibrium**. In this state, even a slight increase in the applied force causes the block to move.
✦   The value of this maximum friction force depends on the nature of the surfaces and the reaction between them, but is independent of the area of contact.
✦   For a given pair of surfaces, the ratio between the limiting friction and the normal reaction is constant.

M1

This constant is called the **coefficient of friction** for the surfaces, and is denoted by μ.

As the friction force is always less than or equal to the limiting friction, you have:

$$\frac{F}{R} \leq \mu \quad \text{or} \quad F \leq \mu R$$

Experiment 3

This uses an alternative approach by which you can try to confirm the values of μ which you found in the first two experiments.

Place one of the blocks on the plank and gradually raise one end of the plank until the block just starts to move. Measure the angle of inclination of the plank.

> You may, in practice, find it easier to measure the length of the plank and the height to which the end is raised, using these to find the sine of the required angle.

Friction is now directed up the slope to try to stop the block sliding down, as shown.

Suppose the block is on the point of moving when the angle is α.

Resolving parallel to the slope gives you:

$$F - Mg \sin \alpha = 0 \qquad [1]$$

Resolving perpendicular to the slope gives you:

$$R - Mg \cos \alpha = 0 \qquad [2]$$

From equation [1], you have: $F = Mg \sin \alpha$ [3]

and from equation [2], you have: $R = Mg \cos \alpha$ [4]

Dividing equation [3] by equation [4], you obtain:

$$\frac{F}{R} = \frac{\sin \alpha}{\cos \alpha} = \tan \alpha$$

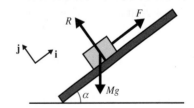

But $F/R = \mu$, the coefficient of friction, so you have:

$$\mu = \tan \alpha$$

You will need to repeat the process several times and average your results to obtain a reasonable value for α and therefore for μ.

Using the author's block on a 39 cm plank, heights (to the nearest 0.5 cm) obtained were 8.5 cm, 7.5 cm, 8 cm, 9.5 cm and 8.5 cm, giving an average height of 8.4 cm and an angle of 12.4°. This estimates the coefficient of friction as:

$$\mu = \tan 12.4° = 0.22$$

> Do **not** worry if in these experiments you obtain results which vary quite widely. It is notoriously difficult to get accurate measurements of friction using simple apparatus. The best you can hope for is to get a general feel for the way friction behaves.

3.6 Static and dynamic friction

In Experiments 1 to 3, you were dealing with **static friction**. That is, the friction available to hold the object stationary. You may have noticed that, once the block started to move, it tended to accelerate, which would indicate that the force exerted by friction when the block is moving is less than that exerted when it is still.

The friction force operating between surfaces moving over one another is called **dynamic** (or **kinetic**) **friction**, and this is usually slightly less than the static friction between the same surfaces.

However, the differences are quite small, and in the M1 module it will be assumed that the coefficients of dynamic and static friction are the same. That is, for a body that is about to move or is moving:

$$F = \mu R$$

Situations in which friction acts on a moving body are dealt with on pages 83–84 and 104–106. For now, the focus is on stationary objects.

Example 9

A block of mass 4 kg rests on a rough horizontal surface. The coefficient of friction between the block and the surface is 0.35. A horizontal force, P, is applied to the block so that it is just on the point of moving. Find the value of P.

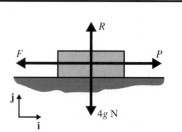

Resolving in the **i**-direction, you get:

$$P - F = 0 \qquad\qquad [1]$$

Resolving in the **j**-direction, you get:

$$R - 4g = 0 \qquad\qquad [2]$$

As friction is limiting, you get:

$$\frac{F}{R} = 0.35 \quad \Rightarrow \quad F = 0.35R \qquad\qquad [3]$$

Substituting from equation [2] into equation [3], you have:

$$F = 0.35 \times 4g = 13.72 \text{ N}$$

And so from equation [1], you obtain $P = 13.72$ N.

Example 10

Using the same block and surface as in Example 9, now apply the force P at an angle of $20°$ to the horizontal. Find the value of P when the block is about to move.

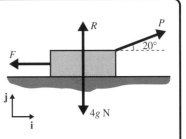

Resolving in the **i**-direction, you get:

$$P \cos 20° - F = 0 \qquad [1]$$

Resolving in the **j**-direction, you get:

$$R + P \sin 20° - 4g = 0 \qquad [2]$$

As friction is limiting, you have:

$$F = 0.35R \qquad [3]$$

From equations [2] and [3], you obtain:

$$F = 0.35 \,(4g - P \sin 20°)$$

Substituting in equation [1], you obtain:

$$P \cos 20° = 0.35(4g - P \sin 20°)$$

$$P = \frac{0.35 \times 4g}{\cos 20° + 0.35 \times \sin 20°} = 12.95 \text{ N}$$

> Note that the force needed at $20°$ is less than the force acting horizontally (Example 9). You may like to consider what happens as the angle increases further still.

M1

Example 11

A block of mass 5 kg rests on a rough horizontal surface. A force of 30 N is applied to the block at an angle of $25°$, as shown. If the block is on the point of moving, find the coefficient of friction between the block and the surface.

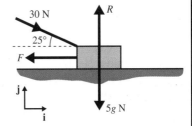

Resolving in the **i**-direction, you get:

$$30 \cos 25° - F = 0 \qquad [1]$$

Resolving in the **j**-direction, you get:

$$R - 5g - 30 \sin 25° = 0 \qquad [2]$$

From equation [1] you obtain: $F = 27.19$ N
From equation [2] you obtain: $R = 61.68$ N

As the block is about to move, $F = \mu R$. So, you have:

$$27.19 = 61.68\mu \quad \Rightarrow \quad \mu = 0.441$$

Example 12

A block of mass m is on a rough plane inclined at $30°$ to the horizontal. The coefficient of friction between the block and the plane is 0.4. A horizontal force P acts on the block. Find the range of possible values of P if the block remains stationary.

The block moves in one of two ways:

a) If P is too small, the block sides down the slope.

b) If P is too large, the block slides up the slope.

a) Suppose the block is in limiting friction and about to slide down the slope. The friction force is directed up the slope to oppose this.

Limiting friction means

$$F = 0.4R \qquad [1]$$

Resolving in the **i**-direction, you get:

$$F + P\cos 30° - mg\sin 30° = 0 \qquad [2]$$

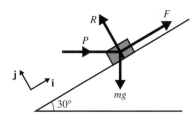

M1

Resolving in the **j**-direction, you get:

$$R - P\sin 30° - mg\cos 30° = 0 \qquad [3]$$

Substituting from equation [1] into equation [2], you obtain:

$$0.4R + 0.866P - 0.5mg = 0 \qquad [4]$$

From equation [3], you have:

$$R - 0.5P - 0.866mg = 0 \qquad [5]$$

Multiplying [5] by 0.4 and then subtracting it from [4], you get:

$$1.066P - 0.154mg = 0$$

$$P = 0.144mg$$

b) Now suppose the block is in limiting friction and about to move up the slope. The friction force is now directed down the slope to oppose this.

Resolving as before, you obtain:

$$P\cos 30° - F - mg\sin 30° = 0 \qquad [1]$$

$$R - P\sin 30° - mg\cos 30° = 0 \qquad [2]$$

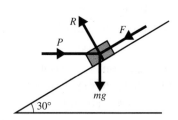

Substituting $F = \mu R$ as before, you get:

$$0.866P - 0.4R - 0.5mg = 0 \qquad [3]$$

$$R - 0.5P - 0.866mg = 0 \qquad [4]$$

Multiplying [4] by 0.4 and then adding it to [3], you obtain:

$$0.666P - 0.846mg = 0$$

$$P = 1.27mg$$

So, the range of values of P is:

$$0.144mg \leqslant P \leqslant 1.27mg$$

Exercise 3C

1 Each of the following diagrams shows a block of mass 5 kg resting on a rough horizontal surface. If the block is in limiting equilibrium, find the coefficient of friction.

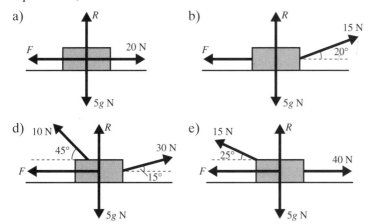

a)   b)   c)

d) 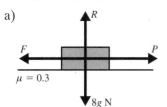   e) 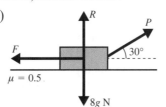   f)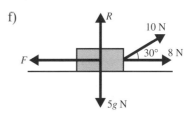

2 Each of the following diagrams shows a block of mass 8 kg resting on a rough horizontal surface. If the block is in limiting equilibrium and the coefficient of friction is as stated, find the force P.

a)   b)   c)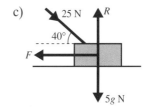

d) 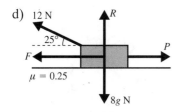   e) 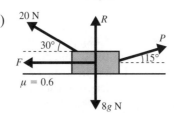   f)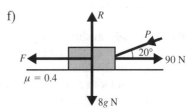

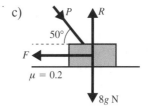

3 A block of mass 5 kg rests in limiting equilibrium on a rough plane inclined at 27° to the horizontal. Find the magnitude of the friction force acting on the block and the coefficient of friction between the block and the plane.

4 A block of mass m rests in limiting equilibrium on a rough plane inclined at an angle α to the horizontal. Show that the coefficient of friction between the block and the plane is tan α.

5 A block of mass 4 kg rests on a rough plane inclined at 10° to the horizontal. The coefficient of friction between the block and the plane is 0.3. A force P acts on the block parallel to the plane. Find the magnitude and direction of P if the block is about to move a) up the plane, b) down the plane.

6 A block of mass 6 kg rests in limiting equilibrium on a rough plane inclined at 20° to the horizontal. Find the horizontal force which would have to be applied to the block to cause it to be on the point of sliding up the plane.

7 An object of mass 50 kg rests on a rough plane inclined at an angle α to the horizontal. It is supported in this position by a light string parallel to the plane which is attached to the object and fixed to a point at the top of the plane. The string has a breaking strain of 200 N, and the coefficient of friction between the object and the plane is 0.2. Find the largest value of α for the string to remain intact.

8 The diagram shows a block of mass 3 kg resting on a smooth plane inclined at 40° to the horizontal. It is connected by a light string passing over a smooth pulley to a second block, of mass 4 kg, which rests on a rough horizontal surface. The system is on the point of moving.

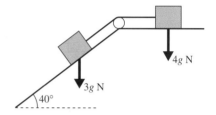

a) By considering the forces acting on the 3 kg block, find the tension in the string.

b) By considering the forces acting on the 4 kg block, find the coefficient of friction between it and the horizontal surface.

9 The diagram shows two blocks resting on rough planes inclined to the horizontal at 40°. The blocks are connected by means of a light string passing over a smooth pulley at the top of the slopes. The coefficient of friction at each block is μ. If the blocks have masses of 10 kg and 4 kg and the system is in limiting equilibrium, find the value of μ.

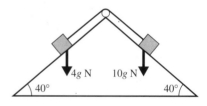

10 The diagram shows particles of mass 2 kg and 1 kg placed on a fixed double inclined plane with inclinations of 60° and 30° respectively. The particles are connected by a light string passing over a smooth pulley at the vertex. The coefficient of friction between the particles and the planes is μ. Show that if the system is on the point of slipping then $\mu = 0.660$.

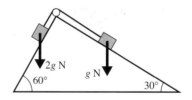

11 A block of mass m rests on a rough plane inclined at an angle α to the horizontal. A force P_1 acting up the plane causes the block to be on the point of moving in that direction. A force P_2 acting down the plane causes the block to be on the point of moving in that direction. Show that $P_1 - P_2$ is independent of the coefficient of friction between the block and the plane.

12 A particle of mass m can just rest on a rough plane inclined at 30° to the horizontal without slipping down. Show that the least horizontal force needed to maintain its position if the inclination is increased to 45° is $0.268mg$.

Summary

You should know how to ...	Check out
1 Recognise the different types of force.	**1** What is a thrust (compression)?
2 Draw a diagram showing all the forces acting on a body.	**2** A block of mass 8 kg lies on a rough horizontal plane. A force of 5 N at 20° to the horizontal acts on the block. Draw a diagram showing all the forces acting on the block.
3 Calculate unknown forces by resolving all the forces present.	**3** A particle of mass 5 kg is supported by two strings, making angles of 30° and 50° to the horizontal. Calculate the tensions in the strings.
4 Calculate the coefficient of friction.	**4** A block of mass 8 kg rests on a rough horizontal plane. When a horizontal force of 10 N is applied, the block is on the point of moving. Find the coefficient of friction.
5 Calculate the maximum friction force possible.	**5** A block of mass 10 kg rests on a rough surface inclined at 30° to the horizontal. The coefficient of friction is 0.3. A horizontal force of 50 N is applied to the block, tending to push the block up the slope. Investigate whether or not the block moves.

M1

Revision exercise 3

1 A load of mass 50 kg is supported, in equilibrium, by two ropes. One is at an angle of 30° to the vertical and the other is horizontal, as shown in the diagram. The tensions in these ropes are T_1 and T_2 newtons respectively.

a) Show that $T_1 = 566$ N, correct to 3 significant figures.

b) Find T_2. (*AQA, 2002*)

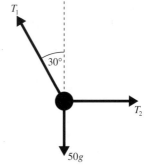

2 An object of mass 100 kg is suspended by two identical cables. The tension in cable one is $(400\mathbf{i} + 300\mathbf{j})$ N, where $\mathbf{i}$ and $\mathbf{j}$ are horizontal and vertical unit vectors respectively. The tension in cable two is $(p\mathbf{i} + q\mathbf{j})$ N.

a) If the object remains at rest, find p and q.

b) State which cable is most likely to break. (*AQA, 2000*)

3 A particle P lies on a smooth horizontal surface. It is acted on
by two horizontal forces of magnitudes 25 N and 20 N. Relative
to horizontal axis P_x, the directions of these two forces
are shown in the diagram. A third horizontal force **F** is required
to keep P in equilibrium.

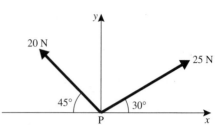

a) Express the force of magnitude 25 N as a vector, giving
its components to one decimal place.

b) Obtain **F** as a vector, giving its components to one
decimal place.

(AQA, 2002)

4 Two cables, AB and AC, are attached to a
cable car, as shown in the diagram. The cable
car has mass 450 kg.

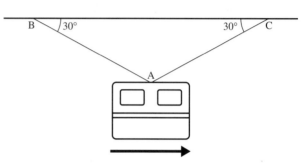

The cable car travels horizontally in the
direction shown by the arrow. Model the cable
car as a particle and assume that there is
no air resistance present. As the cable car
moves, the angles shown in the diagram do
not change.

The cable car travels at a constant speed. Show that the tension in
each cable is 4410 N.

(AQA, 2002)

5 A particle, P, of mass m kg, is held in equilibrium by two strings.
One string is inclined at 50° to the vertical and exerts a force of
60 newtons on the particle. The other string exerts a force of
magnitude T newtons at an angle of 48° to the vertical. The forces
that act on the particle are shown in the diagram.

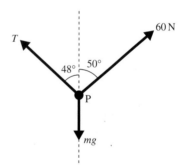

a) Find T.

b) Find m.   *(AQA, 2003)*

6 A particle is at a point O on a smooth horizontal surface. It is
acted on by three horizontal forces of magnitudes 6 N, 8 N and a N.
Relative to horizontal axes Ox and Oy, the directions of these three
forces are shown in the diagram. The resultant, **R**, of these forces
acts along the line Oy.

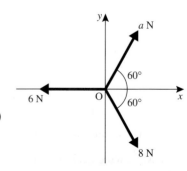

a) Show that $a = 4$.

b) Find the magnitude of **R**.   *(AQA, 2003)*

M1

7 The diagram shows a small box resting on a rough horizontal surface.

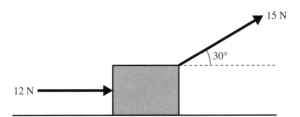

The box is of weight W newtons. It is pushed with a horizontal force of 12 newtons, and pulled with a force of 15 newtons at an angle of 30° to the horizontal.

The box rests in limiting equilibrium.

a) Draw a diagram to show all the forces acting on the box.

b) Show that the frictional force acting on the box is approximately 25 newtons.

c) The coefficient of friction between the box and the surface is $\frac{1}{3}$. Find the normal reaction force between the box and the surface.

d) Find the value of W.

(AQA, 2003)

M1

8 A crate, of mass 50 kg, is at rest on a warehouse floor. The floor is rough and horizontal. The coefficient of friction between the crate and the floor is μ. A rope is attached to the crate at an angle of 30° to the horizontal. The tension in the rope is 100 N. The crate is shown in the diagram.

Model the crate as a particle.

a) Draw and label a diagram to show the forces acting on the crate.

b) Show that the magnitude of the normal reaction force acting on the crate is 440 N.

c) If the crate remains at rest, μ must satisfy the inequality $\mu \geqslant k$. Find k.

(AQA, 2004)

4 Newton's laws of motion

This chapter will show you how to

◆ Use Newton's three laws of motion
◆ Write down the equation of motion of an object under the action of forces
◆ Solve problems involving connected particles

Before you start

You should know how to ...	Check in
1 Manipulate vectors.	**1** Given $\mathbf{u} = 4\mathbf{i} + 7\mathbf{j}$ and $\mathbf{v} = 2\mathbf{i} + 5\mathbf{j}$, find $\mathbf{p}$ if $3\mathbf{p} = 4\mathbf{u} - 2\mathbf{v}$.
2 Use appropriate modelling assumptions.	**2** Two objects, of mass 5 kg and 7 kg, are attached to the ends of a string passing over a pulley. Identify the modelling assumptions which are likely to be made in a first model of the situation.
3 Resolve forces into components.	**3** A force of 60 N acts at 35° to the horizontal. Find the horizontal and vertical components of the force.
4 Solve problems involving friction.	**4** A block of mass 20 kg rests on a rough horizontal plane. The coefficient of friction is 0.4. Calculate the greatest horizontal force which can be applied without moving the block.

Until the 17th century, the accepted model for the motion of objects had not changed significantly since the time of Aristotle, some 2000 years earlier. Essentially, Aristotle believed that for an object to be in motion there must at all times be a force causing that motion. In other words, that force is linked to velocity. For example, when a ball is thrown, Aristotelian mechanics would say that there is a force pushing the ball along throughout its flight.

Newton's contribution was to formalise the idea developing in his time that force was linked not to velocity but to change of velocity: that is, to acceleration. He then calculated how objects should behave according to this model and showed that the results were a good match with observed reality. All the ideas developed in the present book are based on the Newtonian model.

> This is a surprisingly common notion to this day – even in *Star Trek* they seem to keep the engines running all the time, which is quite unnecessary once the required speed is reached!

> Although they are called Newton's *laws*, you should be aware that they are just a mathematical model, albeit a rather good one, of the observable world.

4.1 The first and second laws

First law

> Every object remains at rest or moves with constant velocity unless an external force is applied.

This is really talking about an imbalance of forces. If you start to pull a stationary trolley and someone else pulls in the opposite direction with an equal force, the trolley will stay at rest. If you are pulling the trolley along and the force you are exerting is exactly the same as the friction forces on the trolley, it will move at a constant velocity. It will only speed up, slow down or change direction if all the forces acting on it combine to give a **resultant force**.

The next thing needed is to establish the relationship between the magnitude of the force and the acceleration produced. This problem is addressed by Newton's second law. Newton couched this in terms of momentum, but for your purposes it can be stated as follows.

M1

Second law

> When an object undergoes acceleration, the force needed to produce it is in the direction of the acceleration, and is proportional both to the acceleration and to the mass of the object.

This accords well with common sense in the following respects.

✦ For a given object, a larger acceleration will require a larger force.
✦ The more massive the object, the greater the force needed to achieve a given acceleration.

Symbolically, Newton's second law is expressed as

$$\mathbf{F} \propto m\mathbf{a} \quad \text{or} \quad \mathbf{F} = km\mathbf{a} \quad \text{where } k \text{ is a constant}$$

Notice that this is a relation between vectors because the force and the acceleration have the same direction.

The SI unit of force is the **newton**, which is defined as the force needed to accelerate a 1 kg mass at $1 \, \text{m s}^{-2}$. With this definition, the value of k in the above equation is 1, and Newton's second law becomes

$$\mathbf{F} = m\mathbf{a}$$

This equation is called the **equation of motion** of the body.

Note It cannot be too strongly emphasised that in this equation $\mathbf{F}$ is the **resultant** of the forces acting on the body.

You can express Newton's second law in words:

'Net force equals mass times acceleration.'

Example 1

The engine of a car of mass 900 kg produces a driving force of 2000 N. There are resistive forces of 650 N. Find the acceleration of the car on a level road.

Acceleration takes place in a horizontal direction, so the only forces to consider are those acting horizontally. Resolving horizontally, you get:

Resultant force $= 2000 - 650 = 1350$ N

The equation of motion is $F = ma$, giving

$1350 = 900a$

$a = 1.5 \, \text{m s}^{-2}$ acting horizontally

M1

Note   Strictly, the equation of motion in Example 1 is a vector equation and would formally be written as:

$1350\mathbf{i} = 900\mathbf{a}$

$\mathbf{a} = 1.5\mathbf{i} \, \text{m s}^{-2}$

However, when motion is in a straight line, it is common practice to write the equation in scalar form, as shown.

Example 2

A horizontal force of 50 N is applied to a sledge of mass 20 kg resting on level snow. The sledge accelerates at $2.2 \, \text{m s}^{-2}$. Find the friction force acting on the sledge.

Let the friction force be F.

Resolving horizontally gives the resultant force as $50 - F$ N. So, applying Newton's second law gives:

$50 - F = 20 \times 2.2$

$F = 6$ N

Note There are other forces acting: namely, the weight of the sledge and the normal reaction of the surface. But as there is no vertical acceleration, these forces have a resultant vertical force of zero and so have been ignored.

Example 3

An object of mass 10 kg is acted on by forces $3\mathbf{i} + 6\mathbf{j}$, $2\mathbf{i} - 3\mathbf{j}$ and $\mathbf{i} + 2\mathbf{j}$ relative to some coordinate system. Find the acceleration of the object.

The resultant force acting on the object is:

$(3\mathbf{i} + 6\mathbf{j}) + (2\mathbf{i} - 3\mathbf{j}) + (\mathbf{i} + 2\mathbf{j}) = 6\mathbf{i} + 5\mathbf{j}$

Let the acceleration of the object be **a**. Then, by Newton's second law, you have:

$$6\mathbf{i} + 5\mathbf{j} = 10\mathbf{a}$$
$$\mathbf{a} = 0.6\mathbf{i} + 0.5\mathbf{j}$$

which is the acceleration in vector component form. You can now, if required, find the magnitude and direction of the acceleration:

$$|\mathbf{a}| = \sqrt{0.6^2 + 0.5^2} = 0.781 \text{ m s}^{-2}$$

If θ is the angle with the **i**-direction, then you have:

$$\tan \theta = \frac{0.5}{0.6} \quad \Rightarrow \quad \theta = 39.8°$$

M1

Example 4

A cyclist exerts a driving force of 120 N while travelling at a constant 4 m s^{-1}. The combined mass of cyclist and machine is 80 kg.

a) Find the resistance force acting.

b) If the cyclist increases the driving force to 140 N, find the distance travelled in the next 3 seconds, stating any assumptions made.

. . . .

a) For a constant velocity, the resultant forward force is zero. Therefore, you have:

$$\text{Resistance force} = 120 \text{ N}$$

b) Assuming that the resistance force remains constant, and applying Newton's second law, you obtain:

$$140 - 120 = 80a \quad \text{where } a \text{ is the acceleration}$$
$$a = 0.25 \text{ m s}^{-2}$$

Using $s = ut + \frac{1}{2}at^2$, where s is the distance travelled, $u = 4 \text{ m s}^{-1}$, $t = 3 \text{ s}$ and $a = 0.25 \text{ m s}^{-2}$, you obtain:

$$s = 4 \times 3 + \frac{1}{2} \times 0.25 \times 9$$
$$= 13.125 \text{ m}$$

Therefore, distance travelled in the next 3 seconds is 13.125 m.

Example 5

A truck of mass 500 kg moves along rails under the action of a force P N applied at 20° to the direction of the rails. The safety limit is that the total sideways pressure on the rails should not exceed 500 N. The resistance to the motion of the truck is a constant 1100 N. Find its greatest possible safe acceleration.

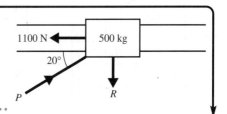

. . . .

Resolving perpendicular to the rails, you have:

$$P \sin 20° - R = 0$$

giving:

$$P = \frac{R}{\sin 20°}$$

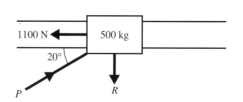

The maximum safe value of R is 500, giving:

Maximum $P = 1461.9$ N

With this value of P, resolve parallel to the rails and apply Newton's second law.

$$1461.9 \cos 20° - 1100 = 500a$$

giving:

$$a = \frac{1461.9 \cos 20° - 1100}{500} = 0.547$$

So, the greatest safe acceleration is $0.547 \, \text{ms}^{-2}$.

M1

Exercise 4A

1 A body of mass 40 kg is acted upon by a resultant force of 90 N. Find the acceleration of the body.

2 Find the force needed to accelerate a body of mass 25 kg at $2.1 \, \text{m s}^{-2}$.

3 A body is acted upon by a resultant force of 24 N and undergoes acceleration of $3.6 \, \text{m s}^{-2}$. What is the mass of the body?

4 A body of mass 4 kg is acted upon by a resultant force of $(12\mathbf{i} + 18\mathbf{j})$ N. Find the acceleration of the body.

5 A particle of mass 3 kg undergoes acceleration of $(2\mathbf{i} - 5\mathbf{j}) \, \text{m s}^{-2}$. What is the resultant force acting on the body?

6 The following table shows information about a vehicle moving on a level road. Find the missing quantities.

	Driving force (N)	Resistance force (N)	Mass (kg)	Acceleration (m s^{-2})
a)	1200	800	500	
b)	2000	600		3.5
c)	900		650	0.8
d)		250	800	1.3
e)	500	800	750	

7 A car of mass 700 kg is acted upon by a driving force of 2200 N and a constant resistance of 800 N. The car starts from rest and travels along a horizontal road. After 6 seconds, the driver depresses the clutch and the car coasts to rest.

a) What was the greatest speed achieved by the car?

b) How far did the car travel altogether?

8 Find, in vector component form, the acceleration of a body of mass 4 kg acted upon by forces $5\mathbf{i} + \mathbf{j}$, $2\mathbf{i} + 7\mathbf{j}$ and $-4\mathbf{i} - 3\mathbf{j}$.

9 A body of mass 2 kg is acted on by forces $2\mathbf{i} + 4\mathbf{j}$, $3\mathbf{i} - 5\mathbf{j}$ and an unknown force $\mathbf{P}$. Find the force $\mathbf{P}$ when the acceleration of the body is $2\mathbf{i} - \mathbf{j}$.

10 Find the magnitude of the resultant force needed to give an object of mass 5 kg an acceleration of $(2\mathbf{i} - 3\mathbf{j})$ m s^{-2}.

M1

11 A horse is towing a truck along rails. The horse is attached to the truck by means of a rope of negligible mass which is horizontal and makes an angle of 20° with the direction of the rails. The truck has a mass of 1200 kg and its motion is opposed by a resistance force of 300 N. Find the tension in the rope if the acceleration of the truck is 0.3 m s^{-2}.

12 Find the magnitude and direction of the acceleration of each of the objects illustrated.

a)

b)

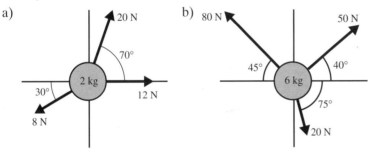

You should specify direction as an angle relative to the positive **i**-direction.

13 Rory, Aurora and Raoul are three lions fighting over a piece of meat of mass 12 kg. Each lion exerts a horizontal pull. Rory pulls with a force of 800 N. Aurora, who is 120° to Rory's right, exerts a force of 400 N. Raoul is 140° to Rory's left. The meat accelerates in Rory's direction.

a) Find the force which Raoul is exerting

b) Find the magnitude of the acceleration.

14 A boat of mass 3 tonnes is steered due east with its engines exerting a driving force of 4000 N. A wind blowing from the south exerts a force of 1200 N. There is a resistance of 2000 N opposing motion. Find the magnitude and direction of the boat's acceleration.

4.2 Exploring Newton's second law further

You can now see the reason for the relation between mass and weight introduced on page 49. An object allowed to fall freely (ideally in a vacuum) near the Earth's surface is observed to accelerate at about 9.8 m s^{-2}. The value varies slightly depending on where the experiment is conducted. It is called the **acceleration due to gravity** and is denoted by g.

Because the object is accelerating, there must be a downward force, W, acting on it. If the mass of the object is m kg, by Newton's second law, you have:

$$W = mg$$

The force W is called the **weight** of the object. It must be stressed that the mass of an object does not vary but its weight depends on the gravitational acceleration it experiences.

For example, an object of mass 10 kg has a weight of $10 \times 9.8 = 98$ N near the Earth's surface. If the object were taken to the Moon, its mass would still be 10 kg but, as gravitational acceleration on the Moon is about 1.6 m s^{-2}, its weight would be $10 \times 1.6 = 16$ N.

Example 6

A crane lifts a 120 kg object on the end of its cable of negligible mass. At first, the object accelerates at 2 m s^{-2}. It then travels at a uniform speed and finally it slows to rest with an acceleration of -1.2 m s^{-2}. Find the tension in the cable at each stage of its motion.

. . . .

The weight of the object is $120 \times 9.8 = 1176$ N

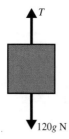

Stage 1 Resolving upwards (taking upwards as the positive direction) and using Newton's second law, you get:

$$T - 1176 = 120 \times 2 \quad \Rightarrow \quad T = 1416 \text{ N}$$

Stage 2 There is no acceleration and thus no resultant force. The tension and the weight must be equal. Therefore, $T = 1176$ N.

Stage 3 Resolving upwards and using Newton's second law, you get:

$$T - 1176 = 120 \times -1.2 \quad \Rightarrow \quad T = 1032 \text{ N}$$

Example 7

An object of mass 8 kg is being towed by a light string up a slope inclined at 20° to the horizontal. The string is inclined at 30° to the slope. There is a frictional resistance of 40 N. The object is accelerating up the slope at 0.8 m s^{-2}.

a) Find the tension in the string.

b) Find the normal reaction exerted by the slope on the object.

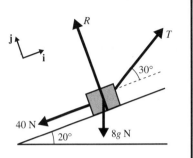

a) Resolving in the **i**-direction and using $F = ma$, you get:

$$T \cos 30° - 40 - 8g \sin 20° = 8 \times 0.8$$
$$T = 84.5 \text{ N}$$

b) Resolving in the **j**-direction there is no acceleration. Therefore, the resultant is zero:

$$R + T \sin 30° - 8g \cos 20° = 0$$

Substituting the value for T in the above equation gives $R = 31.4 \text{ N}$.

M1

In some situations, you will need to adopt the model of friction discussed on pages 63–70 and used here in Examples 7 to 10. If the object is moving, the force of friction must be at its maximum, that is:

$$F = \mu R$$

Example 8

A block of mass 5 kg moves on a rough horizontal plane with coefficient of friction 0.2 under the action of a horizontal force of 30 N. If the block starts from rest, find the distance it travels in the first 3 seconds of motion.

Let the block have acceleration a.

From the laws of friction, you have:

$$F = 0.2R \qquad\qquad [1]$$

Applying Newton's laws and resolving, you obtain:

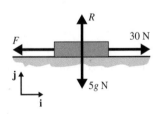

In the **j**-direction: $R - 5g = 0$ [2]

In the **i**-direction: $30 - F = 5a$ [3]

Substituting from equation [2] into equation [1], you have:

$$F = 0.2 \times 5g = 9.8 \text{ N}$$

Substituting in equation [3], you get:

$$20.2 = 5a \quad \Rightarrow \quad a = 4.04 \text{ m s}^{-2}$$

Using $s = ut + \frac{1}{2}at^2$, where $u = 0$, $t = 3$ s and $a = 4.04 \text{ m s}^{-2}$, you obtain:

$$s = \frac{1}{2} \times 4.04 \times 9 = 18.18 \text{ m}$$

So, the block travels 18.18 m in the first 3 s of motion.

Example 9

A particle of mass 6 kg, moving at 8 m s^{-1} on a smooth horizontal surface, goes onto a rough horizontal surface with a coefficient of friction 0.25. Find the distance it moves across the rough surface before coming to rest.

Let the particle have acceleration a.

From the laws of friction, you have:

$F = 0.25R$ [1]

Applying Newton's laws and resolving, you obtain:

In the **j**-direction: $R - 6g = 0$ [2]

In the **i**-direction: $-F = 6a$ [3]

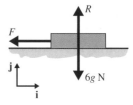

Substituting from equation [2] into equation [1], you get:

$F = 0.25 \times 6g = 14.7\,\text{N}$

Substituting in equation [3], you get:

$-14.7 = 6a \implies a = -2.45\,\text{m s}^{-2}$

Using $v^2 = u^2 + 2as$, where $u = 8\,\text{m s}^{-1}$, $v = 0$ and $a = -2.45\,\text{m s}^{-2}$, you obtain:

$0 = 8^2 - 2 \times 2.45 \times s$

$\implies s = 13.06\,\text{m}$

So, the particle travels a distance of 13.1 m across the rough surface.

Example 10

A block of mass 4 kg is towed along a rough horizontal plane by a string inclined at 20° to the horizontal. The coefficient of friction between the block and the plane is 0.25 and the block is accelerating at 0.5 m s^{-2}. Find the tension in the string.

Resolving vertically, you have:

$R + T\sin 20° - 4g = 0$ [1]

Resolving horizontally and applying Newton's second law, you have:

$T\cos 20° - F = 4 \times 0.5 = 2$ [2]

You also have:

$F = 0.25R$ [3]

Substituting from equation [3] into equation [2] gives:

$T\cos 20° - 0.25R = 2$ [4]

Adding equation [1] to $4 \times$ equation [4] gives:

$T\sin 20° - 4g + 4T\cos 20° = 8$

$T(\sin 20° + 4\cos 20°) = 4g + 8$

$T = \dfrac{4g + 8}{\sin 20° + 4\cos 20°} = 11.5$

So, the tension in the string is 11.5 N.

Exercise 4B

1   Each of the following involves an object of mass of 20 kg moving vertically on the end of a cable. It is assumed that the only forces acting are the weight of the object and the tension in the cable.
    a) Find the acceleration of the object when the tension is
        i) 250 N and ii) 150 N
    b) Find the tension in the cable when the object is:
        i)   moving upwards at a constant speed of 5 m s^{-1}
        ii) moving downwards with a constant speed of 4 m s^{-1}
        iii) accelerating upwards at 2 m s^{-2}
        iv) moving upwards and slowing uniformly from 6 m s^{-1} to 2 m s^{-1} in 6 seconds
        v)   moving downwards and slowing uniformly from 6 m s^{-1} to rest in 8 metres

2   An object of mass 40 kg is suspended by a light string from the ceiling of a lift of mass 200 kg.
    a) The lift accelerates upwards at 1.2 m s^{-2}. Find the tension in the lift cable and the tension in the string.
    b) The string breaks if it suffers a tension of more than 700 N. Find the greatest possible tension in the lift cable if the string remains intact.

3   An object of mass 50 kg is placed on the floor of a lift. Find the reaction between the object and the floor when the lift is:
    a) accelerating upwards at 1.2 m s^{-2}
    b) moving upwards at a constant 3.5 m s^{-1}
    c) moving upwards but slowing uniformly from 5 m s^{-1} to 2 m s^{-1} in 4 seconds
    d) accelerating downwards at 2 m s^{-2}.

4   Bathroom scales actually measure the reaction force between the scales and the person standing on them, but the dial is calibrated to show the mass of the person assuming that the scales are placed in a horizontal position on the surface of the Earth. This means that if the reaction is R, the dial shows the value $R \div 9.8$.

    What reading will the dial show if a person of mass 80 kg stands on the scales in each of the following situations.
    a) On a level surface on the Moon where the acceleration due to gravity is 1.6 m s^{-2}.
    b) On the horizontal floor of a lift accelerating upwards at 1.5 m s^{-2}.
    c) On the horizontal floor of a lift accelerating downwards at 0.8 m s^{-2}.
    d) On the horizontal floor of a lift accelerating upwards at a constant 3 m s^{-1}.
    e) On a surface sloping at 25° to the horizontal.

5   An object of mass 20 kg hangs from a spring balance in a lift. Its apparent mass is 24 kg. What is the acceleration of the lift?

M1

6 An object of mass 12 kg is pulled up a smooth slope, inclined at 45° to the horizontal, by a string parallel to the slope.
   a) If the tension in the string is 120 N, find the acceleration of the object.
   b) If the tension is then reduced so that the object has an acceleration down the slope of $2 \, \text{m s}^{-2}$, find the new tension.

7 A block of mass 3 kg is being towed across a horizontal surface, with coefficient of friction 0.2, by a horizontal force of 18 N. Find the acceleration of the block.

8 A block of mass 5 kg is being towed across a horizontal surface with coefficient of friction μ by a horizontal force of 40 N. If the acceleration of the block is $5 \, \text{m s}^{-2}$, find the value of μ.

9 A block of mass 3 kg is moving at $10 \, \text{m s}^{-1}$ on a smooth horizontal surface when it moves onto a rough horizontal surface with coefficient of friction 0.35. Find the distance which it travels on the rough surface before coming to rest.

> Repeat this question with mass m instead of 3 kg. What happens to the answer?

10 A block of mass 6 kg moves on a rough horizontal surface (coefficient of friction 0.25) under the action of a horizontal force. It accelerates from rest to a speed of $4 \, \text{m s}^{-1}$ in a distance of 12 m, continues for a time at this speed and then decelerates to rest in a distance of 2 m. Find the magnitude and direction of the horizontal force required during each stage of the journey.

11 A particle, moving at $6 \, \text{m s}^{-1}$ on a smooth horizontal surface, goes onto a rough horizontal surface and is brought to rest in a distance of 20 m. Find the coefficient of friction involved.

12 A particle moving on a smooth horizontal surface encounters two rough areas, each 10 m wide. The coefficients of friction for the two areas are 0.2 and 0.4 respectively. Find the minimum initial speed of the particle if it just makes it across the two areas.

13 A box of mass 20 kg rests on a rough horizontal floor, the coefficient of friction being 0.3. A light string is attached to the box and a tension T is exerted with the string inclined upwards at 30° to the horizontal. If the resulting acceleration of the box is $0.5 \, \text{m s}^{-2}$, find the value of T.

14 Find the force needed to accelerate a 2 kg block at $3 \, \text{m s}^{-2}$ up a rough plane (coefficient of friction 0.2) inclined at 25° to the horizontal if the force is
   a) parallel to the slope
   b) horizontal
   c) at 45° to the upward vertical

15 A particle of mass 5 kg is being towed at a constant speed of $6 \, \text{m s}^{-1}$ on a rough horizontal plane with coefficient of friction 0.2. At a certain point the towing force is reversed in direction. Find the distance that the particle will travel before coming to rest and explain what will happen after it does so.

M1

16 A block of mass 10 kg is being towed up a rough slope inclined at 20° to the horizontal. The tow rope is inclined at 20° to the slope and the tension in it is 60 N. The coefficient of friction between the block and the slope is 0.2. Find the acceleration of the block.

17 A block moves on a rough slope of length 10 m inclined at 30° to the horizontal. The coefficient of friction between the block and the slope is 0.4. The block starts from rest at the top of the slope.

a) Find the speed at which the block reaches the bottom of the slope.

The block is then projected back up the slope with an initial speed v ms^{-1}. It just reaches the top of the slope.

b) Find v.

4.3 The third law

M1

> For every action there is an equal and opposite reaction.

This states formally something which will be apparent from your experience of the world. For example, if you stand with a friend of equal mass on an ice rink and one of you pushes the other, you both start to move at an equal speed but in opposite directions.

This is because if an object A exerts a force on a second object B (either by direct contact or at a distance by magnetic attraction, gravitation etc), then B will also exert a force on A. The forces will be of equal magnitude and in opposite directions.

The effect of this is that, if both A on B are part of the system under consideration, the force of A and B and the force of B on A cancel out. They are forces **internal to the system** and do not affect the acceleration of the system. They only become important when you examine the acceleration of object A (or B) alone.

Example 11

A man of mass 90 kg is standing in a lift of mass 300 kg which is accelerating upwards at 0.6 m s^{-2}. Find the tension in the lift cable and the reaction between the man and the floor of the lift.

When finding the tension in the cable, the forces between the man and the lift are internal and need not be considered. The system is just the mass of 390 kg being raised by the cable.

Resolving upwards (taking upwards as the positive direction) and using $F = ma$, you obtain:

$$T - 390g = 390 \times 0.6$$
$$T = 4056 \text{ N}$$

When finding the reaction between the floor and the man, you regard the system as being the man of mass 90 kg acted on by a reaction force R.

Resolving upwards and using $F = ma$, you obtain:

$$R - 90g = 90 \times 0.6$$
$$R = 936 \text{ N}$$

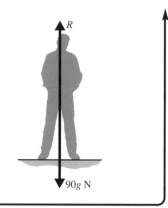

M1 | **Example 12**

An engine of mass 10 tonnes is pulling a truck of mass 3 tonnes. The resistance forces acting on the engine and the truck are 4000 N and 1500 N respectively. The driving force of the engine is 14 000 N. Find the acceleration of the system and the tension in the coupling between the engine and the truck.

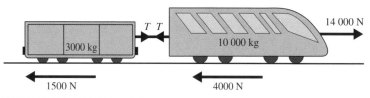

When finding the acceleration, you take the engine and truck as a complete system. So, you need to consider only the driving force and the resistances, because the tension in the coupling is an internal force. You can also ignore the vertical forces.

Resolving horizontally and using $F = ma$, you get:

$$14\,000 - 4000 - 1500 = (10\,000 + 3000)a$$
$$a = 0.654 \text{ m s}^{-2}$$

To find the tension in the coupling, you consider just the forces acting on the truck. So, the tension becomes an external force, as shown.

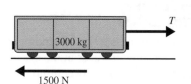

Resolving horizontally and using $F = ma$, you get:

$$T - 1500 = 3000 \times 0.654$$
$$T = 3461.5 \text{ N} = 3460 \text{ N} \quad \text{(to 3 sf.)}$$

Note that you could have just as easily considered the forces on the engine. These would have given:

$$14\,000 - 4000 - T = 10\,000 \times 0.654$$
$$T = 3461.5 \text{ N}$$

4.4 Connected particles

Example 12 involved a situation in which the system comprised two objects connected together. This type of situation is often described as **connected particles**, although the term is usually reserved for situations in which the objects are connected by strings passing over pulleys or other supports. Such situations will now be examined in more detail.

Consider the simplest situation: two objects connected by a string passing over a single pulley. The factors affecting the motion must first be looked at, and a decision taken on the modelling assumptions.

The motion may be affected by the following factors.

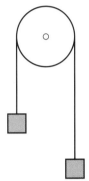

M1

✦ **Mass of the objects.** The difference or similarity of the masses is a crucial factor. If the masses are quite different, some of the other factors may become insignificant.
✦ **Size of the objects.** This will only matter if they are large enough and their speeds great enough for air resistance to play a noticeable part.
✦ **Mass of the string.** A string with significant mass has different tensions at different points along its length. In addition, the amount of mass on either side of the pulley changes as the string moves. The importance of these effects depends on the mass of the string compared with that of the objects.
✦ **'Stretchiness' of the string.** If the string can stretch appreciably, the two objects will not necessarily be going at the same speed or have the same acceleration.
✦ **Friction at the pulley.** If there were no friction in the pulley, the tensions in the string on either side of the pulley would be equal, but friction would cause them to be different.
✦ **Mass and radius of the pulley.** These can be considered together, because they affect the **moment of inertia** of the pulley. This is a concept you will not meet unless you go much further in the study of mechanics, but essentially it measures how much turning force will be 'used up' in accelerating the pulley.
✦ **How the system is set in motion.** If the system does not start with the strings hanging vertically, there may be some pendulum-like movement which could affect the results.

A simple model of the situation makes the following assumptions.

✦ The objects are **particles**. That is, they are small enough to ignore their air resistance.
✦ The string is **light**. That is, its mass is negligible compared with that of the objects.
✦ The string is **inextensible**. That is, its length alters so little under tension that it can be treated as constant.
✦ The pulley is **smooth**. That is, friction at the pulley is insignificant compared with the other forces.
✦ The pulley is **light**. That is, the force needed to accelerate the pulley is negligible.

Example 13

Particles of mass 3 kg and 5 kg are attached to the ends of a light, inextensible string passing over a smooth pulley. The system is released from rest. Find the acceleration of the system and the tension in the string.

First, write down the equation of motion for each of the masses separately:

For the 5 kg mass: $5g - T = 5a$ [1]

For the 3 kg mass: $T - 3g = 3a$ [2]

Then solve these simultaneous equations.

Adding equations [1] and [2], you get:

$$2g = 8a$$
$$a = \tfrac{1}{4}g = 2.45 \text{ m s}^{-2}$$

Substituting the value for a in equation [2], you obtain:

$$T - 3g = \tfrac{3}{4}g$$
$$T = 3\tfrac{3}{4}g = 36.75 \text{ N}$$

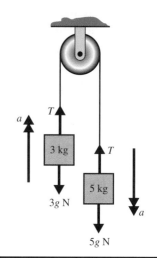

Note on Example 13
The positive direction is chosen separately for each object, rather than set a universal positive direction. This is common practice.

Testing the model

The situation described in Example 13 can be explored experimentally with fairly simple apparatus. The main limitation will probably be your ability to time the motion of the system with sufficient accuracy. The masses used in Example 13 would not be suitable because they are rather large and the predicted acceleration is quite high. The system would move 2 m in about 1.3 seconds, which is too short a time to measure accurately.

If the masses were replaced by, for example, 95 grams and 100 grams, the situation becomes more manageable, moving 2 m in about 4 seconds. You should calculate the predicted acceleration and travel time for various combinations of masses and then compare them with your experimental findings.

If the system moves significantly more slowly than predicted (it should not move faster), you might try to adjust the model. The most obvious additional factor to allow for is the friction in the pulley. The simplest model for this is to assume that it makes the tensions differ by a fixed amount F N. If this had been incorporated into Example 11, the equations of motion would have been:

$$5g - (T + F) = 5a \qquad [1]$$

$$T - 3g = 3a \qquad [2]$$

You could then use your experimental data to find an estimated value for F. This refined model could then be used to predict the behaviour of the system with a new pair of masses, and test these predictions.

It is unlikely that you could go beyond this with a simple experiment, but in theory you could successively refine the model by, for example, examining whether the friction changes with the speed of the system, or by addressing some of the other factors which might affect the motion, until the agreement between prediction and practice is as close as desired.

With these assumptions, it can be stated that the tension is the same throughout the string and that the motions of the objects are the same with regard to acceleration, speed and distance travelled, albeit in opposite directions.

M1

Example 14

A block of mass 4 kg rests on a rough horizontal table, with coefficient of friction 0.5. It is attached by means of a light, inextensible string to a particle of mass 9 kg. The string passes over a smooth pulley at the edge of the table and the 9 kg mass hangs freely. Find the acceleration of the system, the tension in the string and the resultant force acting on the pulley.

First, resolve vertically for the 4 kg mass:

$$R - 4g = 0 \quad \Rightarrow \quad R = 4g \text{ N}$$

As the system will move, the friction force will be at its maximum, so you have:

$$F = 0.5R = 2g \text{ N}$$

You can now write down the equations of motion for the two masses:

For the 9 kg mass: $9g - T = 9a$ [1]
For the 4 kg mass: $T - 2g = 4a$ [2]

From equations [1] + [2], you obtain:

$$7g = 13a \quad \Rightarrow \quad a = 5.28 \text{ m s}^{-2}$$

Substituting into equation [2], you obtain:

$$T - 2g = 21.1 \quad \Rightarrow \quad T = 40.7 \text{ N}$$

To find the force on the pulley, you need to realise that each section of the string exerts a force on the pulley, as shown in the diagram. You therefore have:

Resultant force $= \sqrt{40.7^2 + 40.7^2} = 57.6 \text{ N}$

acting at 45° to the horizontal.

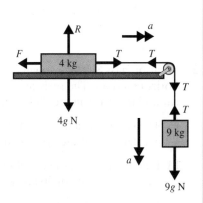

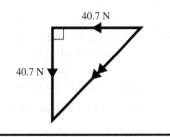

Exercise 4C

1 Two objects of mass 3 kg and 4 kg are connected by a light inextensible string and both can be raised and lowered on the end of a second string, as shown. Find the tensions in the two strings when the system is

3 kg

a) at rest

b) moving upwards at a constant speed of $2 \, \text{m s}^{-1}$

c) moving upwards with acceleration $3 \, \text{m s}^{-2}$

4 kg

2 An object of mass 5 kg is suspended by means of two identical light strings from a rod of mass 3 kg, with the strings making angles of 30° with the horizontal. The rod is suspended by another light string, as shown.

3 kg

30°   30°

a) Find the tensions in the strings if the system is accelerating upwards at $1.5 \, \text{m s}^{-2}$.

5 kg

b) The same type of string is used throughout, with a breaking strain of 120 N. What is the maximum possible upward acceleration of the system and which string will break if this is exceeded?

3 A car of mass 800 kg is towing a caravan of mass 300 kg along a horizontal road. The resistance forces (assumed constant) on the car and the caravan are 700 N and 1200 N respectively.

a) The car exerts a driving force of 3000 N. Find the acceleration of the system and the tension in the coupling.

b) Find the force in the coupling when the system is travelling at a constant speed of $50 \, \text{km h}^{-1}$.

c) Find the force in the coupling when the car exerts a braking force of 2000 N.

4 A block A, of mass 3 kg, is connected by means of a light string to a block B, of mass 4 kg. The blocks are placed on a rough horizontal surface with the string just taut. The coefficient of friction between block A and the surface is 0.4, while for B it is 0.6. A horizontal force is applied to block A in the direction BA, causing the system to accelerate at $1.5 \, \text{m s}^{-2}$.

a) Find the magnitude of the applied force.

b) Find the tension in the string.

5 Two particles of mass 5 kg and 7 kg are connected by a light, inextensible string passing over a smooth pulley. Find:
a) the acceleration of the system
b) the tension in the string
c) the force on the pulley

6 Two particles of mass 2 kg and 3 kg are connected by a light, inextensible string passing over a smooth pulley. The system is released from rest with the 3 kg particle a distance of 4 m above the ground. Find the acceleration of the system and the speed at which the 3 kg particle hits the ground.

7 Two particles of mass m and $2m$ are connected by a light, inextensible string passing over a smooth pulley. Find the acceleration of the system and the tension in the string.

8 A block of mass 3 kg rests on a smooth table. It is connected by a light, inextensible string passing over a smooth pulley at the edge of the table to a 2 kg particle hanging freely. Find the acceleration of the system and the tension in the string.

M1

9 A block of mass 4 kg rests on a table. It is connected by a light, inextensible string passing over a smooth pulley at the edge of the table to a 5 kg particle hanging freely. There is a friction force of 20 N acting on the block. Find the acceleration of the system and the tension in the string.

10 A block of mass 2 kg rests on a smooth table. It is connected by a light, inextensible string passing over a smooth pulley at the edge of the table to a 3 kg particle hanging freely. The block starts from rest at a distance 1.5 m from the pulley. Find the acceleration of the system and the time taken for the block to reach the pulley.

11 A block of mass 4 kg rests on a smooth plane inclined at 20° to the horizontal. It is connected by a light, inextensible string passing over a smooth pulley at the top of the slope to a 3 kg particle hanging freely. Find the acceleration of the system and the tension in the string.

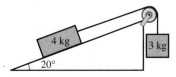

12 Particles A and B of mass 2 kg and 5 kg respectively are connected by a light, inextensible string passing over a smooth pulley. Initially the system is at rest with A on the ground and B at 3 m above the ground. The system is released.
a) Find the acceleration of the system.
b) Find the speed with which the system is moving when B hits the ground.
c) How much further A will rise before coming instantaneously to rest.

13 The diagram shows an object A of mass 5 kg connected by a
light, inextensible string passing over a smooth pulley to a box B
of mass 4 kg. There is an object C of mass 2 kg resting on the
horizontal floor of the box. Find

a) the acceleration of the system

b) the reaction between C and the floor of the box

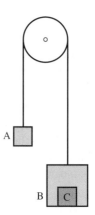

M1

14 The diagram shows a version of what was known as Attwood's
machine, which was used as a means of estimating *g*. Two
objects, both of mass *M*, are connected by a light string passing
over a smooth pulley. The system starts from rest with one of the
masses at A as shown, and a small rider of mass *m* attached to it.
The system moves a distance *h*, at which point the mass *M* passes
through a ring B which removes the rider. The system continues
to move at uniform speed and the mass is timed in its
descent from B to C, a distance *h*. If the system takes a time *t* in
moving from B to C, show that

$$g = \frac{h(2M + m)}{\cdot 2mt^2}$$

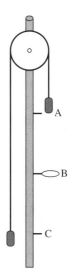

Summary

You should know how to ...	Check out
1 State Newton's three laws of motion.	**1** State Newton's three laws.
2 Use $F = ma$ in the solution of problems.	**2** A body of mass 6 kg is acted upon by forces of $(4\mathbf{i} + 7\mathbf{j})$ N, $(2\mathbf{i} - 3\mathbf{j})$ N and $(6\mathbf{i} + 8\mathbf{j})$ N. Find the acceleration of the body.
3 Use Newton's second and third laws to solve problems involving two or more objects interacting.	**3** A girl of mass 50 kg stands in a lift of mass 400 kg which is accelerating upwards at 0.3 m s^{-2}. a) Find the tension in the lift cable. b) Find the reaction between the girl and the floor of the lift.

4 Solve problems involving pulleys.	**4** Particles of mass 2 kg and 8 kg are attached to the ends of a light, inextensible string passing over a smooth pulley. Find the acceleration of the system and the tension in the string.
5 Solve other problems involving connected particles.	**5** A car of mass 1000 kg pulls a trailer of mass 150 kg along a horizontal road. The resistance forces acting on the car and the trailer are 600 N and 170 N respectively, and the car is accelerating at 0.5 m s^{-2}. a) Find the driving force exerted by the engine. b) Find the tension in the towbar.

M1

Revision exercise 4

1 A motor boat travels in a straight line across a lake. During part of its motion the boat travels with constant acceleration, and its velocity increases from 9 m s^{-1} to 15 m s^{-1} in 4 seconds.

a) i) Find the distance travelled by the boat during this time.
   ii) Show that the acceleration of the boat is 1.5 m s^{-2}.

b) The mass of the boat is 200 kg, and the force of resistance between the water and the boat is 300 N. Find the forward propulsive force of the boat.

(AQA, 2002)

2 A car is initially at rest on a straight, horizontal road. It accelerates uniformly for 8 seconds, reaching a speed of 20 m s^{-1}. It then travels at this constant speed for a further 40 seconds.

a) Sketch a velocity–time graph to illustrate the motion of the car.

b) Find the total distance travelled by the car in the 48 seconds.

c) Show that the acceleration of the car during the first 8 seconds is 2.5 m s^{-2}.

d) A driving force of magnitude P newtons acts on the car in the direction of motion. A constant resistance force of magnitude 600 newtons acts on the car throughout its motion. The mass of the car is 1200 kg.
   i) State the value of P when the car is travelling at a constant speed.
   ii) Find the value of P when the car is accelerating at 2.5 m s^{-2}.

(AQA, 2002)

3 Two constant forces $\mathbf{F}_1 = (4\mathbf{i} + 16\mathbf{j})$ N and $\mathbf{F}_2 = (6\mathbf{i} - 11\mathbf{j})$ N act on a particle. A force $\mathbf{F}_3$ also acts on the particle. The mass of the particle is 8 kg and the unit vectors $\mathbf{i}$ and $\mathbf{j}$ are perpendicular.

a) In the case when the particle moves with a constant velocity, find $\mathbf{F}_3$.

b) In the case when the acceleration of the particle is $(2\mathbf{i} + 3\mathbf{j})$ m s^{-2}, find the magnitude of $\mathbf{F}_3$.

(AQA, 2001)

4 Two particles, of masses 0.3 kg and 0.4 kg, are connected by a light inextensible string which hangs over a smooth fixed peg, as shown in the diagram. The system is released from rest.

a) i) Show that, in the subsequent motion, the acceleration of the particles is of magnitude 1.4 m s^{-2}.

ii) Find the tension in the string during this motion.

b) Find the distance travelled by each particle during the first 2 seconds of the motion.   *(AQA, 2001)*

5 Two particles, of masses 0.3 kg and m kg, are connected by a light, inextensible string which hangs over a smooth fixed peg, as shown in the diagram. The system is released from rest. During the subsequent motion, the 0.3 kg mass moves upwards and the tension in the string is 3.36 N.

a) Show that the magnitude of the acceleration of the particles is 1.4 m s^{-2}.

b) Find the value of m.

c) Find the magnitude of the force the string exerts on the peg.   *(AQA, 2002)*

6 Two particles are connected by a light string that passes over a smooth, light pulley, as shown in the diagram.

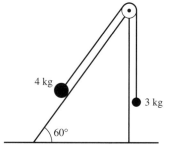

The 4 kg particle is on a smooth, fixed slope, which is at an angle of 60° to the horizontal. The 3 kg particle hangs with the string vertical.

The particles are released from rest at the position shown.

a) Show that the acceleration of the particles is approximately 0.65 m s^{-2}.

b) By considering the 3 kg particle, determine the tension in the string.   *(AQA, 2002)*

7 The diagram shows a car pulling a trailer in a straight line on a horizontal stretch of road.

The mass of the car is 1250 kg and the total resistance force acting on the car is 500 N.

The mass of the trailer is 250 kg and the total resistance force acting on the trailer is 100 N.

a) During part of the journey, a constant braking force is applied to the car, causing the car and trailer to decelerate at a constant rate of 0.5 m s^{-2}.

i) By considering the forces on the trailer, find the magnitude of the force in the towbar between the car and the trailer.

ii) Find the magnitude of the braking force applied to the car.

b) Later in the journey, the car and trailer travel with constant speed. State the magnitude of the tension in the towbar.   *(AQA, 2003)*

M1

8 A car moves along a straight road. When it passes a set of traffic lights, the car is travelling at a speed of 8 m s^{-1}. The car then moves with constant acceleration for 10 seconds and travels 200 metres.

a) Show that the acceleration of the car is 2.4 m s^{-2}.

b) Find the speed of the car at the end of the 10 seconds.

c) The road is horizontal and the car has mass 1200 kg. A constant resistance force of 1800 N acts on the car while it is moving.

   i) Find the magnitude of the driving force that acts on the car while it is accelerating.

   ii) At the end of the 10 second period, the driving force is removed. The car then moves subject to the resistance force of 1800 N until it stops. Find the distance that the car travels while it is slowing down.

(AQA, 2002)

M1

9 Two children are holding the ends of a light, inextensible rope, which passes over a light, smooth pulley. Initially Tom, who has a mass of 40 kg, is standing at ground level and Simon, who has a mass of 60 kg, is on the edge of a fixed platform 2 metres above ground level. Model the two boys as particles, one initially at ground level, and the other initially at a height of 2 metres. The rope is taut.

Simon steps off the platform and as he falls vertically, Tom rises vertically.

a) Assume that the rope remains taut while the boys are moving.

   i) Show that the acceleration of each boy is 1.96 m s^{-2}.

   ii) Find the tension in the rope.

b) Find the total distance that Tom travels upwards.

(AQA, 2003)

10 A block, of mass 6 kg, rests on a rough, horizontal surface. The coefficient of friction between the block and the surface is 0.2. A light, inextensible, string attached to the block passes over a smooth pulley. A weight, of mass 2 kg, hangs from the other end of the string, as shown in the diagram.

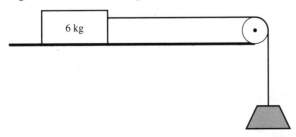

Find the tension in the string and the acceleration of the block.

(AQA, 2000)

11 A block, of mass 6 kg, is held at rest on a rough horizontal table. The block is attached, by a light string that passes over a light smooth pulley, to a sphere of mass 4 kg, that hangs freely, as shown in the diagram.

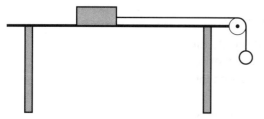

a) The block is released and travels 60 cm in 2 seconds. Show that the acceleration of the block is 0.3 m s^{-2}.

b) Find the magnitude of the tension in the string.

c) Find the magnitude of the friction force that acts on the block.

d) Find the coefficient of friction between the block and the table. Give your answer correct to two significant figures.

(AQA, 2001)

12 A skier slides in a straight line directly down a slope inclined at 30° to the horizontal. The coefficient of friction between her skis and the slope is 0.3. The skier and her equipment are to be modelled as a particle of mass 80 kg. Assume that there is no air resistance present.

a) Draw a diagram to show the forces acting on the skier.

b) i) Find the magnitude of the normal reaction force acting on the skier.

   ii) Show that the magnitude of the friction force acting on the skier is 204 N to three significant figures.

c) Find the acceleration of the skier.

(AQA, 2003)

13 Two particles are connected by a light inextensible string, which passes over a smooth fixed peg, as shown in the diagram. The particle A, of mass 0.5 kg, is in contact with a rough horizontal surface, and the particle B, of mass 0.2 kg, hangs freely. The coefficient of friction between A and the surface is $\frac{2}{7}$.

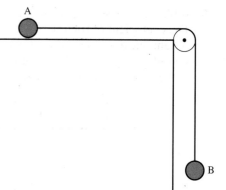

The system is released from rest with the string taut and A moves towards the peg.

a) Show that the frictional force between A and the surface is of magnitude 1.4 N.

b) Find the acceleration of the particles.

c) Find the tension in the string.

d) Find the time taken for the particles to travel 0.625 metres, given that A has not then reached the peg.

(AQA, 2002)

14 A sledge, of mass 12 kg, is pulled up a rough slope
which is inclined at an angle of 10° to the horizontal.
The coefficient of friction between the slope and the
sledge is 0.2.

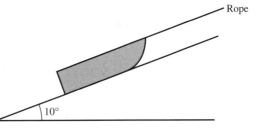

a) The sledge is pulled by a rope that is parallel to
the slope, as shown in the diagram.
  i) Draw a diagram to show the forces acting on
      the sledge.
  ii) Find the magnitude of the normal reaction
      force acting on the sledge.
  iii) Given that the acceleration of the sledge is 0.5 m s^{-2},
      show that the tension in the rope is approximately
      50 N.

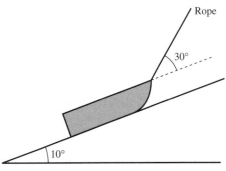

b) The sledge is then pulled with the rope at an angle of
30° to the slope, as shown in the diagram. Find the
acceleration of the sledge if the tension in the rope
is 60 N.

c) Write down **two** modelling assumptions that you
have made.   (*AQA, 2002*)

M1

5 Linear momentum

This chapter will show you how to

◆ Understand the concept of momentum
◆ Calculate the momentum of a body
◆ Use the principle of conservation of momentum

Before you start

M1

You should know how to ...	Check in
1 Identify the difference between a scalar and a vector.	1 Classify each of the following as a scalar or a vector: a) velocity, b) displacement and c) distance.
2 Solve equations involving vectors.	2 Find $\mathbf{v}$, given that: $$3(2\mathbf{i} + 4\mathbf{j}) + 7(\mathbf{i} - \mathbf{j}) = 3(4\mathbf{i} + \mathbf{j}) + 7\mathbf{v}$$

5.1 Concept of momentum

Linear momentum of a particle

The linear momentum of a particle is defined as follows.

> Linear momentum = Mass × Velocity

The term 'linear' is needed to distinguish this from the angular momentum of a rotating body. When there is no possibility of confusion, it is usual to drop the term and refer just to the momentum of a particle.

The unit of momentum is the **newton second (N s)**.

You can see the reason for this if you consider an object, initially at rest, which is accelerated uniformly to a velocity $\mathbf{v}$ m s^{-1} in a time t s.

For constant acceleration, you have:

$$\mathbf{v} = \mathbf{u} + \mathbf{a}t$$

which, in this case, gives:

$$\mathbf{v} = \mathbf{a}t$$

Therefore, the momentum is:

$$m\mathbf{v} = m\mathbf{a}t$$

But from Newton's second law of motion, $m\mathbf{a}$ is the accelerating force. So, momentum is equivalent to a force × a time. Hence, its unit is the newton second.

Notice that, as velocity is a vector quantity, momentum is also a vector quantity. For example, a particle of mass 5 kg travelling with velocity $(2\mathbf{i} - 3\mathbf{j})$ m s^{-1} has:

$$\text{Momentum} = 5(2\mathbf{i} - 3\mathbf{j}) = (10\mathbf{i} - 15\mathbf{j}) \text{ N s}$$

Momentum of a system of particles

If you are considering a system comprising two or more particles, you can speak of the momentum of the system. This is the vector sum of the momentums of the individual particles.

For example, if a system consists of a 3 kg mass travelling with velocity $(4\mathbf{i} + \mathbf{j})$ m s^{-1} and a 4 kg mass travelling with velocity $(\mathbf{i} - 2\mathbf{j})$ m s^{-1}, you have:

$$\text{Momentum of system} = 3(4\mathbf{i} + \mathbf{j}) + 4(\mathbf{i} - 2\mathbf{j})$$
$$= (16\mathbf{i} - 5\mathbf{j}) \text{ N s}$$

M1

Conservation of linear momentum

According to Newton's first law of motion, the velocity of a system will not change unless an external force acts on it.

The velocities of the individual particles in the system may change as a result of interactions between them. This could happen in a variety of ways, three examples of which are given below.

◆ Two of the particles might collide.
◆ Particles may be connected by a string, or by elastic, which becomes taut.
◆ There may be magnetic attraction or repulsion between particles.

Suppose two particles, masses m_1 and m_2, are involved in such an interaction. Each will be subjected to a force and by Newton's third law these forces will be equal and opposite. They will also act for the same length of time, t.
Suppose the average forces are $\mathbf{F}$ and $-\mathbf{F}$ respectively.
The first particle undergoes an acceleration $\mathbf{a}_1$.
By Newton's second law, $\mathbf{F} = m_1\mathbf{a}_1$.
If the particle has initial velocity $\mathbf{u}_1$ and final velocity $\mathbf{v}_1$, its change of momentum is:

$$m_1\mathbf{v}_1 - m_1\mathbf{u}_1 = m_1(\mathbf{v}_1 - \mathbf{u}_1) = m_1\mathbf{a}_1 = \mathbf{F}t$$

Similarly, for the second particle $-\mathbf{F} = m_2\mathbf{a}_2$, and its change of momentum is:

$$m_2(\mathbf{v}_2 - \mathbf{u}_2) = m_2\mathbf{a}_2t = -\mathbf{F}t$$

You can see that the changes in momentum for the two particles are equal and opposite. The total momentum of the two particles has not been changed by the interaction.

In all such interactions between particles in a system, the forces are internal to the system. They change the momentum of the particles, but their effect on the total momentum of the system is zero. The momentum of the system can only be changed by a force external to the system.

This gives the **principle of conservation of linear momentum**, which is expressed as follows.

> The total momentum of a system remains constant unless an external force is applied.

For example, imagine two ice skaters, of equal mass (m), standing facing each other. If either skater pushes the other, experience tells you that they both start to move. In fact, Newton's third law of motion tells you that the skaters receive equal and opposite forces. The skaters will move in opposite directions, but with the same speed, v.

That is, you have:

Momentum before push $= 0$
Momentum after push $= mv + m(-v) = 0$

M1   So, the total momentum of the system formed by the two skaters is unchanged.

Example 1

A particle, of mass 4 kg and travelling at $6\,\text{m s}^{-1}$, collides with a second particle, of mass 3 kg and travelling in the opposite direction at $2\,\text{m s}^{-1}$. After the collision, the first particle continues in the same direction but with its speed reduced to $1\,\text{m s}^{-1}$. Find the velocity of the second particle after the collision.

Let the velocity of the second particle after the collision be v.

Total momentum before collision $= 4 \times 6 + 3 \times (-2)$
$= 18\,\text{N s}$
Total momentum after collision $= 4 \times 1 + 3v = 3v + 4$

There are no external forces, so momentum is conserved.

Therefore, you have:

$3v + 4 = 18 \quad \Rightarrow \quad v = 4\frac{2}{3}\,\text{m s}^{-1}$

Before collision

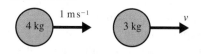

After collision

Example 2

A body A, of mass 5 kg, is travelling with velocity $6\,\text{m s}^{-1}$. It catches up and collides with a body B, of mass 3 kg, which is travelling along the same line with velocity $4\,\text{m s}^{-1}$. After collision, the bodies coalesce (merge into a single body). Find the velocity after collision.

Let v be the velocity of the combined body after impact.

Momentum before collision $= 5 \times 6 + 3 \times 4 = 42\,\text{N s}$
Momentum after collision $= 8v$

There are no external forces, so momentum is conserved.
Therefore, you have:

$8v = 42 \quad \Rightarrow \quad v = 5.25\,\text{m s}^{-1}$

Before collision

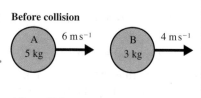

After collision

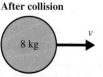

Example 3

A rail truck, of mass 4 tonnes, is travelling along a straight, horizontal rail at 4 m s^{-1}. It meets another truck, of mass 2 tonnes, travelling in the opposite direction at 5 m s^{-1}. The trucks collide and become coupled together. Find their combined velocity after collision.

Take left to right to be the positive direction.

Let the combined velocity after collision be v.

Momentum before $= 4000 \times 4 + 2000 \times (-5)$
$= 6000$ N s

Momentum after $= 6000v$

There are no external forces in the direction of motion and so momentum is conserved. Therefore, you have:

$6000v = 6000 \Rightarrow v = 1$ m s^{-1}

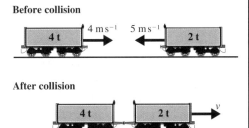

Before collision

After collision

M1

Example 4

A body of mass 4 kg travelling with velocity $(3\mathbf{i} + 2\mathbf{j})$ m s^{-1} collides and coalesces with a second body of mass 3 kg travelling with velocity $(\mathbf{i} - 3\mathbf{j})$ m s^{-1}. Find their common velocity after impact.

Let the common velocity after impact be $\mathbf{v}$.

Total momentum before collision $= 4(3\mathbf{i} + 2\mathbf{j}) + 3(\mathbf{i} - 3\mathbf{j})$
$= (15\mathbf{i} - \mathbf{j})$ N s

Total momentum after collision $= 7\mathbf{v}$

By the principle of conservation of momentum, you have:

$7\mathbf{v} = 15\mathbf{i} - \mathbf{j}$

$\mathbf{v} = (2\frac{1}{7}\mathbf{i} - \frac{1}{7}\mathbf{j})$ m s^{-1}

Example 5

Two particles, A and B, lie at rest on a smooth horizontal table. They are connected by a light inextensible string which is initially slack. A has a mass of 3 kg and B 2 kg. B is set in motion with velocity 8 m s^{-1} in the direction AB. Find the common velocity of the particles immediately after the string goes taut.

Let the common velocity be v.

Total momentum before $= 2 \times 8 = 16$ N s
Total momentum after $= 2v + 3v = 5v$

There are only internal forces acting, so momentum is conserved. Therefore, you have:

$5v = 16 \Rightarrow v = 3.2$ m s^{-1}

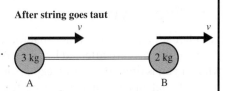

Before string goes taut

8 m s^{-1}

After string goes taut

Example 6

A block of wood of mass 2.95 kg rests on a rough horizontal surface with coefficient of friction 0.4. It is struck horizontally by a bullet of mass 0.05 kg travelling at 90 m s^{-1}, which becomes embedded in the block. Find the distance travelled by the block before it comes to rest.

....

Let the common velocity of the block and bullet after the impact be v.

You have:

Momentum before impact $= 0.05 \times 90 = 4.5$ N s
Momentum after impact $= (2.95 + 0.05)v = 3v$

Assume that the impact occurs over such a short period of time that friction has no appreciable effect on v. Hence, momentum is conserved, giving:

$3v = 4.5 \quad \Rightarrow \quad v = 1.5$ m s^{-1}

Once the impact has taken place, the block is sliding on the horizontal surface and being slowed by the friction force.

Resolving vertically, you get:

$R - 3g = 0$
$R = 3g$ N   [1]

Resolving horizontally and using Newton's second law, you obtain:

$-F = 3a$ [2]

The object is moving, hence friction is limiting. So, from equation [1], you have:

$F = 0.4R = 1.2g$ N

Substituting into equation [2], you obtain:

$-1.2g = 3a$
$a = -0.4g$ m s^{-2}

You therefore have a block with initial velocity 1.5 m s^{-1} slowing to rest with constant acceleration $- 0.4g$ m s^{-2}. Using $v^2 = u^2 + 2as$, you have:

$0 = 1.5^2 - 0.8gs$

$\therefore \quad s = \dfrac{2.25}{0.8g} = 0.287$ m

So, the block comes to rest after 0.287 m.

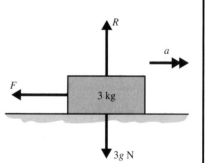

5.2 Explosive forces

Another situation in which internal forces act upon parts of a system is when the parts are affected by an explosive force. For example, when a gun is fired, there is an explosion which exerts a forward force on the bullet and an equal backward force on the gun. If the gun is free to move, it will make a sudden backwards movement – the recoil.

No external force is involved, so the momentum of the system is conserved. Usually, the gun is stationary before firing, and so the total momentum of the system is zero before and after the shot is fired.

Example 7

A bullet of mass 50 g is fired horizontally from a gun of mass 1 kg, which is free to move. The bullet is fired with a velocity of 250 m s^{-1}. Find the speed with which the gun recoils.

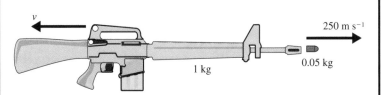

Both the gun and the bullet are stationary before the shot is fired, so the initial momentum is zero.

Take left to right as the positive direction, and let the recoil speed be v.

First, find the momentum after firing:

Momentum after firing $= 0.05 \times 250 + 1(-v) = 12.5 - v$

Momentum is conserved, so you have:

$12.5 - v = 0$

$v = 12.5 \text{ m s}^{-1}$

Example 8

A gun of mass 800 kg fires a shell of mass 4 kg horizontally at 400 m s^{-1}. The gun rests on a rough horizontal surface, and the coefficient of friction between the gun and the surface is 0.6. The gun is stationary before the shot is fired. Find the distance which the gun will move as a result of firing.

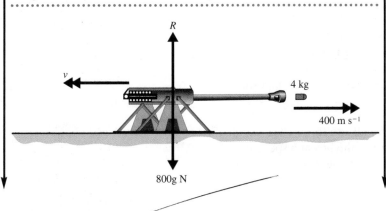

The gun is stationary before firing, so the total initial momentum is zero.

Take left to right to be positive, and the recoil speed to be v.

First, find the momentum after firing:

$$\text{Momentum after firing} = 4 \times 400 + 800(-v) = 1600 - 800v$$

Assume that the explosion is of sufficiently short duration, whereby the force of friction is negligible compared with that of the explosion. Therefore, the situation is one in which there is effectively no external force and so momentum is conserved. So, you have:

$$1600 - 800v = 0$$
$$v = 2\,\text{m s}^{-1}$$

Resolving vertically, you get:

$$R - 800g = 0 \quad \Rightarrow \quad R = 800g\,\text{N}$$

The friction force, F, is given by $F = \mu R$. So, you have:

$$F = 0.6R \quad \Rightarrow \quad F = 480g\,\text{N}$$

Resolving horizontally, Newton's second law gives:

$$-480g = 800a$$
$$a = 0.6g\,\text{m s}^{-2}$$

The gun has an initial velocity of $2\,\text{m s}^{-1}$, a final velocity of zero and an acceleration of $-0.6g\,\text{m s}^{-2}$. Using $v^2 = u^2 + 2as$, you have:

$$0 = 4 - 1.2gs$$
$$s = \frac{4}{1.2g} = 0.340\,\text{m}$$

So, the gun moves $0.340\,\text{m}$.

M1

Exercise 5A

1   A bullet of mass 40 grams is fired horizontally with velocity $600\,\text{m s}^{-1}$ into a block of wood of mass 6 kg, which is resting on a smooth horizontal surface. The bullet becomes embedded in the block. Find the common speed of the bullet and block which results.

2   Two particles, A and B, have masses of 2 kg and 3 kg respectively. They are travelling at speeds of $5\,\text{m s}^{-1}$ and $2\,\text{m s}^{-1}$ respectively. They collide and coalesce (merge together). Find their common speed after the collision if, before they collided, they were travelling a) in the same direction; b) in opposite directions.

3   Arthur balances a box on top of a wall and throws a snowball of mass 0.3 kg at it. The snowball strikes the box at a speed of $10\,\text{m s}^{-1}$ and sticks to it. Their common speed after impact is $4\,\text{m s}^{-1}$. Find the mass of the box.

4 A railway truck of mass $3m$, travelling at a speed of $2v$, collides
with another of mass $4m$, travelling at a speed of v. The trucks
become coupled together. Find, in terms of v, the common
speed of the trucks after impact under each of the following
conditions.

a) They are travelling in the same direction.

b) They are travelling in opposite directions.

5 A particle A, of mass 10 kg, is moving at 5 m s^{-1} when it collides
with a particle B, of mass m kg, travelling in the opposite
direction at 2 m s^{-1}. After the collision, A travels in the same
direction as before but with its speed reduced to 3 m s^{-1}.

a) If $m = 3$, find the velocity of B after the collision.

b) Show that the value of m cannot be greater than 4.

M1

6 Arnold (mass 50 kg) is standing on a trolley (mass 20 kg) which
is stationary. Bernice is standing behind the trolley. She throws
Arnold a package of mass 5 kg, which he catches while it is
travelling horizontally at 4 m s^{-1}, causing the trolley to start
moving forwards. He immediately throws it horizontally back
towards Bernice at a speed of 5 m s^{-1}. Find the speed of the
trolley at the end of this process.

7 A sledgehammer of mass 6 kg, travelling at 20 m s^{-1}, strikes the
top of a post of mass 2 kg and does not rebound.

a) Find the common speed of the hammer and post
immediately after the impact.

b) If the post is driven 15 cm into the ground by the impact, find
the average resistance of the ground to the motion of the
post.

8 A bullet of mass 50 g is fired horizontally at a wooden block of
mass 4 kg, which rests on a rough horizontal surface. The
coefficient of friction between the block and the surface is 0.4.
As a result of the collision, the block, with the bullet embedded,
moves a distance of 10 m along the surface before coming to
rest. Find the speed at which the bullet enters the block.

9 Masses of 3 kg and 5 kg are connected by an elastic rope and are
held apart on a smooth horizontal surface with the rope
stretched. The masses are released from rest and a short time
later the smaller mass has a speed of 6 m s^{-1}. Find the speed of
the larger mass at that time.

10 A gun of mass 500 kg, which is free to move, fires a shell of mass
5 kg horizontally at a speed of 200 m s^{-1}. Find the speed of recoil
of the gun.

11 A gun of mass 400 kg fires a shell of mass 8 kg horizontally at a speed of 300 m s^{-1}. Find the restraining force, assumed constant, which will be needed to bring the gun to rest in a distance of 2 m.

12 An object of mass 2 kg and velocity $(2\mathbf{i} - \mathbf{j})$ m s^{-1} strikes and coalesces with a second object of mass 3 kg and velocity $(4\mathbf{i} + 6\mathbf{j})$ m s^{-1}. Find their common velocity after impact.

13 An object of mass 4 kg, travelling with velocity $(5\mathbf{i} + 2\mathbf{j})$ m s^{-1}, is struck by a second object of mass 6 kg and velocity $\mathbf{v}$, which sticks to it. Their common velocity afterwards is $(2\mathbf{i} - 4\mathbf{j})$ m s^{-1}. Find $\mathbf{v}$.

14 An object of mass 3 kg has velocity $(3\mathbf{i} + 2\mathbf{j})$ m s^{-1}. It collides with another object, which has a mass of 2 kg and a velocity of $(\mathbf{i} - \mathbf{j})$ m s^{-1}. After the impact, the first object has a velocity of $(2\mathbf{i} + \mathbf{j})$ m s^{-1}. Find the velocity of the second object.

15 A particle of mass 4 kg has a velocity of $(\mathbf{i} - \mathbf{j})$ m s^{-1}. It collides with a second particle, which has a mass of m kg and a velocity of $(2\mathbf{i} - 3\mathbf{j})$ m s^{-1}. The first particle is brought to rest by the impact, and the second particle has a velocity of $(4\mathbf{i} + a\mathbf{j})$ m s^{-1}. Find the values of m and a.

Summary

You should know how to ...	Check out
1 Find the momentum of a particle.	**1** a) A particle of mass 3 kg is moving with a velocity of 8 m s^{-1}. Calculate its momentum.
	b) A particle of mass 5 kg is moving with a velocity of $(4\mathbf{i} - 2\mathbf{j})$ m s^{-1}. Calculate its momentum.
2 Apply the principle of conservation of momentum to find the velocity of a body after collision.	**2** a) A particle, of mass $3m$ and travelling with a velocity of $(4\mathbf{i} - 7\mathbf{j})$ m s^{-1}, collides with a second particle, of mass $2m$ and travelling with a velocity $(5\mathbf{i} + \mathbf{j})$ m s^{-1}. The particles coalesce. Find the velocity of the combined body after the collision.
	b) A particle A, of mass 2 kg and travelling with a speed of 5 m s^{-1}, collides with a particle B, of mass 6 kg and travelling in the opposite direction with a velocity of 2 m s^{-1}. B's direction of travel is reversed by the collision, and its speed is then 1 m s^{-1}. Find what happens to A.

M1

Revision exercise 5

1 A stone, A, of mass 0.05 kg, is sliding in a straight line with speed
3 m s^{-1} across a smooth frozen pond when it collides directly with
a stationary stone, B, of mass 0.2 kg. After the collision, A and B
move directly **away** from each other, each with speed $v \text{ m s}^{-1}$.

Find the value of v.   (*AQA, 2002*)

2 A particle P has mass 5 kg. It is moving along a straight line with
speed 4 m s^{-1}, when it collides directly with another particle Q
which is at rest. The mass of Q is m kg.

M1

After the collision, P moves with a speed of 1.2 m s^{-1} and
Q moves with a speed of 1.4 m s^{-1}.

a) If P and Q both move in the same direction after the
collision, show that $m = 10$.

b) If P and Q move in opposite directions after the collision, find m.   (*AQA, 2002*)

3 Two particles, A and B, of masses $2m$ kg and m kg respectively, are
moving directly **towards** each other on a smooth horizontal surface.
The speeds of A and B are 2 m s^{-1} and 6 m s^{-1} respectively.

The particles A and B collide and subsequently move directly **away**
from each other with speeds $3V \text{ m s}^{-1}$ and $V \text{ m s}^{-1}$ respectively.

Find the value of V.   (*AQA, 2003*)

4 A particle A of mass 0.3 kg is moving with velocity $\begin{pmatrix} 7 \\ 4 \end{pmatrix} \text{ m s}^{-1}$ when
it collides with a stationary particle, B, of mass 0.5 kg. Immediately
after the collision, B moves with velocity $\begin{pmatrix} 6 \\ 0 \end{pmatrix} \text{ m s}^{-1}$.

a) Find the velocity of A immediately after the collision.

b) Find the speed of A immediately after the collision.

c) State which of A and B moves faster after the collision.   (*AQA, 2002*)

5 A particle A, of mass 0.1 kg, is moving with velocity $\begin{pmatrix} 2 \\ 5 \end{pmatrix} \text{ m s}^{-1}$ when
it collides with another particle B, of mass m kg, which is moving
with velocity $\begin{pmatrix} -1 \\ 0 \end{pmatrix} \text{ m s}^{-1}$. After the collision, A and B move with

velocities $\begin{pmatrix} 1 \\ c \end{pmatrix} \text{ m s}^{-1}$ and $\begin{pmatrix} 3 \\ 4 \end{pmatrix} \text{ m s}^{-1}$ respectively.

a) Find the value of m.

b) Find the value of c.   (*AQA, 2002*)

6 Three particles A, B and C are set into motion along a straight line on a smooth horizontal surface. A has mass 3 kg and initially moves at $3 \, \text{m s}^{-1}$. B has mass 2 kg and initially moves in the same direction as A at $2 \, \text{m s}^{-1}$. C has mass 5 kg and initially moves in the opposite direction to A and B at $1 \, \text{m s}^{-1}$. The initial velocities and positions are shown in the diagram.

a) The particles A and B collide and join together. Show that the combined particle moves with a speed of $2.6 \, \text{m s}^{-1}$ after the collision.

b) When the combined particle collides with the particle C, they join together. Find the velocity of this new combined particle after this collision.

c) After the second collision, a force acts on the new combined particle for 0.2 seconds and brings it to rest. Find the magnitude of this force.

(AQA, 2003)

7 A test is carried out on a rocket, of mass 200 kg, which is fired horizontally at a speed of $50 \, \text{m s}^{-1}$. The rocket experiences a constant air resistance force of 1568 N. It travels a distance of 108 metres before it hits a stationary tank, of mass 4800 kg. Assume that the rocket always travels horizontally.

a) Find the speed of the rocket when it has travelled a distance of 108 metres.

When the rocket hits the tank it becomes lodged in it.

b) Find the speed of the tank and the rocket just after the collision.

The tank then slides until it comes to rest. The coefficient of friction between the tank and the ground is 0.6. Neglect any air resistance when considering the motion of the tank and rocket together.

c) Find the distance that the tank slides.

(AQA, 2001)

8 A sledge, of mass 10 kg, is at rest on an icy, horizontal surface. A child, of mass 40 kg, is standing on the sledge.

The child jumps off the sledge. Initially, the child travels horizontally at $2 \, \text{m s}^{-1}$ and the sledge begins to slide in the opposite direction to the child.

a) Assuming that momentum is conserved, find the speed of the sledge, just after the child has jumped off it.

b) The coefficient of friction between the sledge and the ice is 0.2.
   i) Find the magnitude of the friction force acting on the sledge while it is moving.
   ii) Find the distance that the sledge slides before it comes to rest.

(AQA, 2002)

6 Projectiles

This chapter will show you how to

◆ Model the motion of a projectile fired from ground level or from a point above ground level

◆ Calculate the range, time of flight and maximum height of such a projectile

Before you start

You should know how to ...	Check in
1 Substitute into formulae.	**1** Using $y = vt \sin \alpha - \frac{1}{2}gt^2$, find the value of y when $v = 40$, $\alpha = 45°$, $t = 2$ and $g = 9.8$.
2 Solve algebraic equations.	**2** If $h = \dfrac{u^2 \sin^2 \theta}{2g}$, find θ when $h = 50$, $g = 9.8$ and $u = 40$.
3 Solve a quadratic equation by applying the quadratic formula.	**3** Find t when $-5 = 20t - 4.9t^2$.

This chapter is concerned with the problem of modelling the motion of an object moving freely through the air under gravity. Unless the object is buffeted by strong side winds, it is effectively moving in two dimensions. A typical projectile situation will be explored.

6.1 Setting up the model

1 The real problem

Consider a shot putter at an athletics meeting. The shot putter is interested in achieving the maximum distance, and the factors under his/her control are the speed and angle of projection of the shot.

2 Factors affecting distance shot travels

There are at least six factors which play a part in the distance the shot travels. They are:

◆ Angle of projection
◆ Mass of shot
◆ Speed of projection
◆ Air resistance
◆ Height of shot putter
◆ Physical build of shot putter

Simplifying assumptions

In order to simplify the model, the following assumptions are made:

- ✦ The shot is a particle.
- ✦ There is no air resistance.
- ✦ The shot putter has zero height, so that the point of projection is at ground level.
- ✦ The ground is a horizontal plane.

Variables and parameters

The point of projection will be taken as the origin, and the following symbols used:

$\mathbf{i}, \mathbf{j}$ Horizontal and vertical unit vectors

$\mathbf{r}$ Displacement of shot at time t, where $\mathbf{r} = x\mathbf{i} + y\mathbf{i}$

U Initial speed of shot

θ Angle of projection

m Mass of shot

g Acceleration due to gravity

3 Formulating the mathematical model

Once the shot is released, the only force acting on it is its weight, $-mg\mathbf{j}$. Hence, the equation of motion (Newton's second law) is:

$$-mg\mathbf{j} = m\mathbf{a}$$
$$\mathbf{a} = -g\mathbf{j} \qquad\qquad [1]$$

Thus, the acceleration of the shot is constant and vertically downwards.

4 Solving the mathematical model

The motion is completely described if expressions can be found for the displacement (position) and velocity of the shot at time t. As the acceleration is constant, the equations of motion for uniform acceleration can be used.

The initial velocity, $\mathbf{u}$, is given by:

$$\mathbf{u} = U \cos \theta \mathbf{i} + U \sin \theta \mathbf{j}$$

Using $\mathbf{v} = \mathbf{u} + \mathbf{a}t$ gives:

$$\mathbf{v} = (U \cos \theta \mathbf{i} + U \sin \theta \mathbf{j}) - gt\mathbf{j}$$
$$\mathbf{v} = U \cos \theta \mathbf{i} + (U \sin \theta - gt)\mathbf{j} \qquad [2]$$

Equation [2] gives the velocity of the shot at time t.

Using $\mathbf{r} = \mathbf{u}t + \frac{1}{2}\mathbf{a}t^2$ gives:

$$\mathbf{r} = (U \cos \theta \mathbf{i} + U \sin \theta \mathbf{j})t - \frac{1}{2}gt^2\mathbf{j}$$
$$\mathbf{r} = Ut \cos \theta \mathbf{i} + (Ut \sin \theta - \frac{1}{2}gt^2)\mathbf{j} \qquad [3]$$

Equation [3] gives the displacement of the shot at time t.

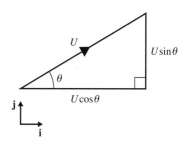

The range

The shot putter is interested in the range. That is, the horizontal displacement achieved by the shot by the time that it hits the ground. An expression can be obtained for this from equation [3], as follows.

You have:

$$\mathbf{r} = x\mathbf{i} + y\mathbf{j} = Ut \cos \theta\, \mathbf{i} + (Ut \sin \theta - \tfrac{1}{2}gt^2)\, \mathbf{j}$$

When the shot hits the ground $y = 0$, giving:

$$Ut \sin \theta - \tfrac{1}{2}gt^2 = 0$$
$$t(U \sin \theta - \tfrac{1}{2}gt^2) = 0$$
$$t = 0 \quad \text{or} \quad t = \frac{2U \sin \theta}{g}$$

The value $t = 0$ corresponds to the time of projection, so the shot hits the ground when $t = \dfrac{2U \sin \theta}{g}$.

The horizontal displacement is given by $x = Ut \cos \theta$, so, when the shot hits the ground, you have:

$$\text{Range} = \frac{2U^2 \sin \theta \cos \theta}{g} \qquad [4]$$

> You can explore the effects on the range of changing the values of U and θ by downloading the spreadsheet PROJECTILE1 from the OUP website. Just type in the address:
> http://www.oup.co.uk/secondary/mechanics

Some facts can be deduced from the form of the foregoing expression.

You will be aware that $\sin (90° - \theta) = \cos \theta$ and $\cos (90° - \theta) = \sin \theta$. This means that the range expression takes the same value for angles of projection θ and $(90° - \theta)$. For example, the model predicts that a shot putt at 30° to the horizontal will have the same range as one putt at 60° (at the same speed, of course).

From this, it can be deduced that the maximum range will occur when $\theta = (90° - \theta)$: that is, when $\theta = 45°$.

5 Comparing with reality

It would be quite difficult to test these conclusions experimentally with a real shot putter. In fact, one of the assumptions – the putter has zero height – is quite implausible. The effect of removing this assumption will be explored on page 117. However, for other situations where an object **is** projected from ground level, such as a ball being kicked, it can be shown experimentally that, for small objects and low speeds, the model developed above provides realistic results.

M1

Example 1

A golf ball is hit towards the hole with a velocity of 50 m s^{-1} at an angle of 30° to the horizontal. The hole is 180 m from the point at which the ball is hit. Assuming horizontal ground, how far from the hole will the ball land?

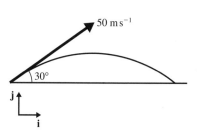

Assume that the ball is a particle, that there is no air resistance and that $g = 9.8$ m s^{-2}.

Take unit vectors as shown in the diagram.

The initial velocity, **u**, of the ball is given by:

$$\mathbf{u} = 50 \cos 30° \,\mathbf{i} + 50 \sin 30° \,\mathbf{j}$$
$$\mathbf{u} = 25\sqrt{3}\mathbf{i} + 25\mathbf{j}$$

The acceleration of the ball is $-9.8\,\mathbf{j}$. So, using $\mathbf{r} = \mathbf{u}t + \frac{1}{2}\mathbf{a}t^2$, you get:

$$\mathbf{r} = (25\sqrt{3}\mathbf{i} + 25\mathbf{j})t - 4.9t^2\mathbf{j}$$
$$\mathbf{r} = 25\sqrt{3}t\mathbf{i} + (25t - 4.9t^2)\mathbf{j}$$

The vertical displacement of the ball is $y = 25t - 4.9t^2$, and the ball hits the ground when $y = 0$. Therefore, you have:

$$25t - 4.9t^2 = 0$$
$$t(25 - 4.9t) = 0$$
$$t = 0 \quad \text{or} \quad t = 5.1$$

The value $t = 0$ corresponds to the striking of the ball, so the ball lands when $t = 5.1$.

The horizontal displacement of the ball is $x = 25\sqrt{3}t$. So, the distance travelled by the ball is:

$$25\sqrt{3} \times 5.1 = 220.9 \text{ m}$$

Hence, the ball lands 40.9 m beyond the hole.

> **Note** In Example 1, the expression derived for the range of a projectile (page 112) could be used. However, in the examination you will be expected to find the maximum height from the basic equations. Just quoting formulae is not acceptable.

6.2 Exploring the model further

On page 111, the following equations are derived for the velocity and displacement of a projectile:

$$\mathbf{v} = U \cos \theta \,\mathbf{i} + (U \sin \theta - gt)\mathbf{j} \qquad [2]$$
$$\mathbf{r} = Ut \cos \theta \,\mathbf{i} + (Ut \sin \theta - \tfrac{1}{2}gt^2)\mathbf{j} \qquad [3]$$

These equations have already been used to find an expression for the range. They will now be used to solve two further problems: finding the maximum height reached by the projectile, and finding the equation of the flight path.

Maximum height

The projectile is at the highest point of its flight when the vertical component of velocity is zero. That is:

$$U \sin \theta - gt = 0$$
$$t = \frac{U \sin \theta}{g}$$

M1

Notice that, according to the model presented here, this is exactly half the time the projectile spends in the air.

The vertical displacement is $y = Ut \sin \theta - \frac{1}{2}gt^2$. Substituting the expression for t gives:

$$y = \frac{U^2 \sin^2 \theta}{g} - \frac{U^2 \sin^2 \theta}{2g} = \frac{U^2 \sin^2 \theta}{2g}$$

So, you have:

> Maximum height $= \dfrac{U^2 \sin^2 \theta}{2g}$

In the examination, you will be expected to derive your results from the basic equations. Just quoting formulae is not acceptable.

Example 2

M1

A boy kicks a ball from the ground with a velocity of 12 m s⁻¹ at an angle of 60° to the horizontal. Can the ball clear a fence 5 m high?

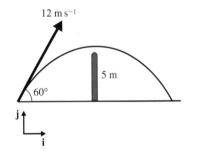

Make the following assumptions:

✦ There is no air resistance
✦ The position of the fence corresponds to the highest point in the ball's trajectory

Taking unit vectors as shown in the diagram, the initial velocity, **u**, is given by:

$$\mathbf{u} = 12 \cos 60° \, \mathbf{i} + 12 \sin 60° \, \mathbf{j}$$
$$\mathbf{u} = 6\mathbf{i} + 10.4\mathbf{j}$$

The acceleration is $\mathbf{a} = -9.8\mathbf{j}$. Using $\mathbf{v} = \mathbf{u} + \mathbf{a}t$, the velocity of the ball at time t is given by:

$$\mathbf{v} = (6\mathbf{i} + 10.4\mathbf{j}) - 9.8t\mathbf{j}$$
$$\mathbf{v} = 6\mathbf{i} + (10.4 - 9.8t)\mathbf{j}$$

The ball reaches maximum height when the vertical velocity component is zero. That is, when:

$$10.4 - 9.8t = 0 \quad \Rightarrow \quad t = 1.06$$

Using $\mathbf{r} = \mathbf{u}t + \frac{1}{2}\mathbf{a}t^2$, the displacement of the ball at time t is given by:

$$\mathbf{r} = (6\mathbf{i} + 10.4\mathbf{j})t - 4.9t^2\mathbf{j}$$
$$\mathbf{r} = 6t\mathbf{i} + (10.4 - 4.9t^2)\mathbf{j}$$

The maximum height is the vertical component of displacement when $t = 1.06$. Therefore, you have:

$$\text{Maximum height} = 10.4 \times 1.06 - 4.9 \times 1.06^2 = 5.51 \text{ m}$$

Thus, the ball can clear the fence, provided that it is at or near its maximum height as it passes over the fence.

Example 3

A ball is kicked with a velocity of 10 m s^{-1} at an angle of 40° to the horizontal towards a wall which is 7 m away.

a) How far up the wall does the ball hit?

b) What is the speed of the ball when it hits the wall?

c) In what direction is the ball moving when it hits the wall?

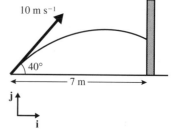

Make the usual assumptions.

With unit vectors as shown in the diagram, you have:

      Initial velocity: $\mathbf{u} = 10\cos 40°\,\mathbf{i} + 10\sin 40°\,\mathbf{j}$

      Acceleration: $\mathbf{a} = -9.8\mathbf{j}$

Using $\mathbf{v} = \mathbf{u} + \mathbf{a}t$, the velocity at time t is given by:

      $\mathbf{v} = (10\cos 40°\,\mathbf{i} + 10\sin 40°\,\mathbf{j}) - 9.8\,t\mathbf{j}$

      $\mathbf{v} = 7.660\,\mathbf{i} + (6.428 - 9.7t)\mathbf{j}$

Using $\mathbf{r} = \mathbf{u}t + \frac{1}{2}\mathbf{a}t^2$, the displacement at time t is given by:

      $\mathbf{r} = (10\cos 40°\,\mathbf{i} + 10\sin 40°\,\mathbf{j}) - 4.9t^2\mathbf{j}$

      $\mathbf{r} = 7.660t\,\mathbf{i} + (6.428t - 4.9t^2)\mathbf{j}$

a) The horizontal displacement of the ball at time t is $7.660t$. When the ball has travelled 7 m horizontally to hit the wall, you have:

      $7.660t = 7 \;\Rightarrow\; t = 0.9138$

The height of the ball at time t is $6.428t - 4.9t^2$. So, when the ball hits the wall, you have:

      Height $= 6.428 \times 0.9138 - 4.9 \times 0.9138^2 = 1.78$ m (to 3 sf)

b) The velocity of the ball at this point is:

      $\mathbf{v} = 7.660\mathbf{i} + (6.428 - 9.8 \times 0.9138)\mathbf{j}$

      $\mathbf{v} = 7.66\mathbf{i} - 2.53\mathbf{j}$

The speed at impact is the magnitude of this velocity. So, you have:

      $v = \sqrt{7.66^2 + 2.53^2} = 8.07$ m s^{-1}

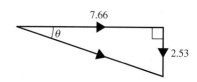

c) The direction of the motion is given by the angle θ in the diagram, where:

      $\tan\theta = \dfrac{2.53}{7.66} \;\Rightarrow\; \theta = 18.3°$

So, when the ball hits the wall, it is travelling in a direction 18.3° below the horizontal.

Revising the model

Finally, look again at the problem of the shot putter. Originally it was assumed that the putter had zero height, so that the shot started from the origin. This gave an expression for the displacement at time t:

      $\mathbf{r} = Ut\cos\theta\,\mathbf{i} + \left(Ut\sin\theta - \frac{1}{2}gt^2\right)\mathbf{j}$ [3]

Now assume that the shot is released at a height h above the ground. This means that the displacement from the origin at time t is altered by an amount $h\mathbf{j}$, giving:

$$\mathbf{r} = Ut \cos \theta \mathbf{i} + \left(h + Ut \sin \theta - \tfrac{1}{2}gt^2\right)\mathbf{j} \qquad [7]$$

The height, y, above the ground is therefore given by $y = h + Ut \sin \theta - \tfrac{1}{2}gt^2$, and so the shot hits the ground when:

$$h + Ut \sin \theta - \tfrac{1}{2}gt^2 = 0$$

This problem will be solved for the particular case in Example 5. If you wish to explore the model further, you should download the spreadsheet PROJECTILE2 from the Oxford University Press website (http://www.oup.co.uk/mechanics). You should find that the angle of projection required for maximum range is no longer 45°.

M1

Example 4

A shot putter releases the shot at a height of 2.5 m and with a velocity of 10 m s^{-1} at 50° to the horizontal. Find the distance travelled by the shot.

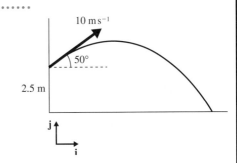

The initial velocity, $\mathbf{u}$, of the shot is given by:

$$\mathbf{u} = 10 \cos 50° \, \mathbf{i} + 10 \sin 50° \, \mathbf{j}$$

Using $\mathbf{r} = \mathbf{u}t + \tfrac{1}{2}\mathbf{a}t^2$, its displacement *from its point of projection* at time t is:

$$\begin{aligned}\mathbf{r} &= (10 \cos 50° \, \mathbf{i} + 10 \sin 50° \, \mathbf{j})t - 4.9t^2\mathbf{j} \\ &= 10t \cos 50° \, \mathbf{i} + (10t \sin 50° - 4.9t^2)\mathbf{j}\end{aligned}$$

Hence, its displacement *from the origin* at time t is:

$$\mathbf{r} = 10t \cos 50° \, \mathbf{i} + (2.5 + 10t \sin 50° - 4.9t^2)\mathbf{j}$$

The height, y, of the shot above the ground is:

$$y = 2.5 + 10t \sin 50° - 4.9t^2$$

So, the shot hits the ground when:

$$\begin{aligned}2.5 + 10t \sin 50° + 4.9t^2 &= 0 \\ 4.9t^2 - 7.66t - 2.5 &= 0\end{aligned}$$

Solving this quadratic equation gives $t = -0.277$ or $t = 1.84$. The negative root can be discarded in the context of the problem, so the shot hits the ground after 1.84 s.

The horizontal displacement, x, is given by $x = 10t \cos 50°$. So, when the shot hits the ground, you have:

$$x = 10 \cos 50° \times 1.84 = 11.8$$

Hence, the shot has a range of 11.8 m.

Exercise 6A

1 A projectile is launched from ground level with a speed of
15 m s^{-1} at an angle of 35° to the horizontal.
a) For how long is the projectile in the air?
b) What is the horizontal range of the projectile?
c) Find the time taken to reach maximum height.
d) What is the greatest height reached?

2 A projectile is launched from ground level with a speed of
10 m s^{-1} at an angle of 60° to the horizontal.
a) For how long is the projectile in the air?
b) What is the horizontal range of the projectile?
c) Find the time taken to reach maximum height.
d) What is the greatest height reached?

M1

3 A particle is projected from a point at ground level with a speed
of 24 m s^{-1} at an angle of 50° to the horizontal. A wall is situated
30 m away from the projection point.
a) Find how far up the wall the particle hits it.
b) What is the speed of the particle when it hits the wall?
c) Find the direction of motion of the particle when it hits the wall.

4 A ball is projected with a velocity of (30**i** + 40**j**) from a point on
the ground.
a) Find the position of the ball 1 s and 2 s later.
b) How long would the ball stay in the air if the ground were level?
c) Find the range of the ball.

5 A particle is fired at a speed of 196 ms^{-1}, and at an angle α to
the horizontal. If the particle reaches a maximum height of
490 m, find the value of α.

6 A particle is projected at 45° to the horizontal from a point on
level ground, and strikes the ground again 100 m away. Find the
speed with which it was projected.

7 A particle is projected with a velocity whose horizontal and
vertical components are v_x and v_y respectively. The highest point
of its flight is 12 m above and 32 m horizontally from the point of
projection. Find v_x and v_y and hence the initial speed and angle
of the particle.

8 A ball is kicked from the floor of a gym at 40° to the horizontal and
at a speed of V m s^{-1}. The ceiling of the gym is 10 m above the floor.
a) Find in terms of V the maximum height to which the ball rises.
b) Hence find the greatest value of V for which the ball does not
hit the ceiling.
c) For this value of V find the distance the ball travels before
hitting the floor.
d) State the main assumptions you have made.

9 A stone is thrown horizontally from the top of a 50 m high
vertical cliff at 30 m s^{-1}. Find how far from the foot of the cliff
the stone hits the sea.

10 A dart is thrown horizontally at 21 m s^{-1} towards a board 3 m away. The point of projection of the dart is at the same level as the bull's-eye on the board.
a) Find the length of time the dart takes to reach the board.
b) Find the distance below the bull's-eye at which the dart strikes the board.
c) At what angle to the horizontal is the dart travelling at the moment that it strikes the board?

11 A ball was projected at an angle of 60° to the horizontal. One second later another ball was projected from the same point at an angle of 30° to the horizontal. One second after the second ball was released, the two balls collided. Show that the velocities of the balls were 12.99 m s^{-1} and 15 m s^{-1}. Take the value of g to be 10 m s^{-2}.

12 Two projectiles are released simultaneously from the same point with the same speed, one at an angle of elevation θ, and the other at an angle of elevation α. Show that, during flight:
a) the line joining the two particles has a constant gradient
b) the distance between them is increasing at a constant rate.

M1

Summary

You should know how to ...	Check out
1 Find the components of velocity for a projectile.	**1** A particle is projected at an angle α to the horizontal and with speed u. Write down its horizontal and vertical components of velocity and displacement at time t.
2 Find the time of flight of a projectile.	**2** A ball is kicked with velocity 15 m s^{-1} at an angle of 50° to the horizontal. Find the time before the ball hits the (horizontal) ground.
3 Find the maximum height reached by a projectile.	**3** Find the maximum height reached by the ball in Question 2.
4 Find the range of a projectile.	**4** Find the range of the ball in Question 2.
5 Solve problems in which the point of projection is at a different height from the point of landing.	**5** A ball is thrown from a point 8 m above a horizontal plane, with a velocity of 12 m s^{-1} at an angle of 40° above the horizontal. Find each of the following. a) The time of flight of the ball. b) The horizontal distance from the point of projection to the landing point.
6 Find the equation of the path of a projectile.	**6** A particle is projected with velocity $(30\mathbf{i} + 20\mathbf{j}) \text{ m s}^{-1}$, where $\mathbf{i}$ and $\mathbf{j}$ are the horizontal and vertical directions. Find the equation of the path of the particle.

Revision exercise 6

1 A javelin is modelled as a particle. Assume that only gravity acts on the javelin after it has left the thrower's hand. The initial velocity of the javelin is 20 m s^{-1} at an angle of $40°$ above the horizontal.

a) Find the range of the javelin on horizontal ground if the height of release is ignored.

b) The javelin is actually released at a height of 2 metres. Find the range of the javelin in this case.

(AQA, 2001)

2 A golfer hits a ball, from ground level on a horizontal surface. The initial velocity of the ball is 21 m s^{-1} at an angle of $60°$ above the horizontal. Assume that the ball is a particle and that no resistance forces act on the ball.

a) Find the maximum height of the ball.

b) Find the range of the ball.

c) Find the speed of the ball at its maximum height.

(AQA, 2001)

3 A golf ball is struck at a point O on the ground and moves with an initial velocity of 20 m s^{-1} at an angle of $53°$ to the horizontal. The ball subsequently lands at a point X which is on the same horizontal level as O.

a) Show that the time taken by the ball to reach the point X is approximately 3.26 seconds.

b) Calculate the distance OX.

c) State:

   i) the least speed of the ball during its flight from O to X

   ii) the direction of motion of the ball when this least speed occurs.

(AQA, 2002)

4 A particle is projected from a horizontal surface at a speed V and an angle α above the horizontal.

a) Prove that the maximum height of the particle is $\dfrac{V^2 \sin^2 \alpha}{2g}$.

b) A ball is hit from ground level. The ball initially moves at an angle of $60°$ above the horizontal. The maximum height of the ball is 6 metres above the ground. Modelling the ball as a particle:

   i) find the initial speed of the ball

   ii) find the range of the ball.

(AQA, 2003)

5 During a game of football, Tom kicks the ball towards the goal.
He kicks the ball with velocity $(8\mathbf{i} + 7\mathbf{j})$ m s^{-1}, from a point O
which is 10 metres from the goal. The height of the top of the
goal is 2.44 metres.

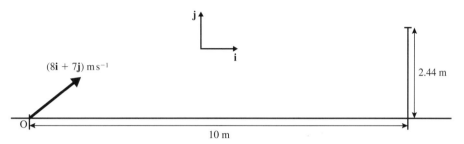

The unit vectors $\mathbf{i}$ and $\mathbf{j}$ are horizontal and vertically upwards
respectively, as shown in the diagram.

a) Show that the time the ball takes to reach the goal is
    1.25 seconds.

b) Determine whether the ball passes under or over the top of
    the goal.

c) Find the speed of the ball when it reaches the goal, giving
    your answer to two significant figures.

    (AQA, 2001)

M1

6 The diagram shows a cross-section of a court where Oliver is
practising tennis shots. The court is of length 26 metres, and the
net, situated at N, the centre of the court, is of height 1 metre.
Oliver stands at the point O at one end of the court. Oliver
serves the ball from a height of 2.225 metres above O with a
horizontal velocity U m s^{-1}.

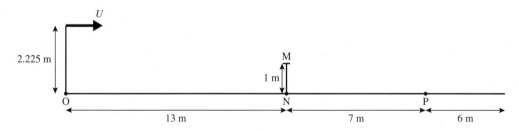

a) When $U = u_1$, the ball strikes point M, at the top of the net.

   i) By considering the vertical component of the motion of
       the ball, show that the time taken for the ball to reach M
       is 0.5 seconds.

   ii) Hence, find the value of u_1.

b) When $U = u_2$, where $u_2 > u_1$, the ball first hits the court
    between the points N and P, where NP = 7 metres.

    Show that $u_2 < 30$.

    (AQA, 2002)

7 A golf ball is hit from a position that is 4 metres higher than the horizontal area where the ball lands. The initial velocity of the ball is 30 m s^{-1} at an angle of 60° above the horizontal.

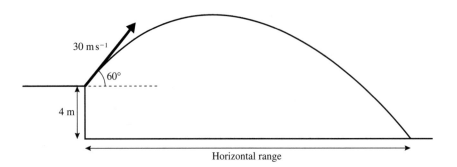

a) Show that the maximum height of the ball, above the landing area, is approximately 38.4 metres.

b) Show that the ball hits the ground approximately 5.45 seconds after it has been hit.

c) Hence calculate the horizontal range of the ball, to the nearest metre.

(AQA, 2002)

8 Paul throws a ball from a point O with a velocity of 21 m s^{-1} at an angle of α to the horizontal, where $\sin \alpha = 0.7$. The ball subsequently moves freely under gravity in a vertical plane, as shown in the diagram.

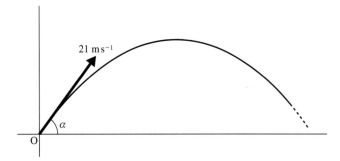

a) Show that the time taken for the ball to reach its greatest height above O is 1.5 seconds.

b) When the ball reaches its greatest height, it passes over a tree of vertical height 8 metres, as shown in the diagram below.

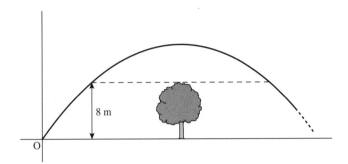

8 m

O

M1

i) Find the vertical distance between the ball and the top of the tree at this time.

ii) Find the time between the ball leaving O and first reaching the horizontal level of the top of the tree. Give your answer to two decimal places.

iii) Find the length of time for which the ball is above the horizontal level of the top of the tree.

(AQA, 2003)

9 The diagram shows a target that is used for rifle shooting. It consists of three concentric circles of radii 15 cm, 25 cm and 40 cm respectively.

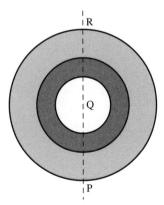

R

Q

P

When the rifle is fired it is always 50 metres from the target and at the same height as the centre of the target. The bullet moves in the vertical plane that contains the line PR. The bullet is assumed not to be subject to any air resistance.

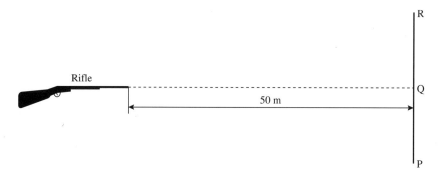

A bullet is fired horizontally. It hits the target on the outer circle at the point P. Show that the bullet was fired at a speed of 175 m s^{-1}.

(AQA, 2002)

M1 Practice Paper (Option A)

75 minutes   60 marks   You may use a graphics calculator.

*Answer **all** questions.*

1 A stone is released from rest and falls vertically a distance of
40 metres before hitting the ground.

   a) Calculate the velocity of the stone as it hits the ground. *(2 marks)*

   b) Calculate the time between the stone being released and it
hitting the ground. *(2 marks)*

2 a) A particle P moves with constant velocity. P passes through the
points with position vectors $\begin{pmatrix} -1 \\ 4 \end{pmatrix}$ and $\begin{pmatrix} 7 \\ 8 \end{pmatrix}$ at times $t = 0$ and

     $t = 4$ respectively. Show that the velocity of P is $\begin{pmatrix} 2 \\ 1 \end{pmatrix}$ m s^{-1}. *(3 marks)*

   b) When $t = 4$, the particle P, of mass 3 kg, collides with a
particle Q of mass 2 kg. Immediately before the collision Q is

     moving with velocity $\begin{pmatrix} 7 \\ -4 \end{pmatrix}$ m s^{-1}.

     As a result of the collision, P and Q coalesce into a single
particle, R. Find the velocity of R immediately after the
collision. *(4 marks)*

3 The graph shows how the velocity, v m s^{-1}, of a train varies with
time, t seconds, as it moves along a straight horizontal track
between two stations. The journey takes 210 seconds.

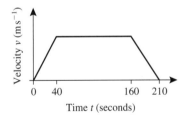

   a) The train starts from rest with a constant acceleration of
0.5 m s^{-2}. Find its maximum speed. *(2 marks)*

   b) Find the average speed of the train between the two
'stations. *(6 marks)*

4 Two forces, $\mathbf{F}_1 = 5\mathbf{i} + 12\mathbf{j}$ and $\mathbf{F}_2 = 7\mathbf{i} - 3\mathbf{j}$, act on a particle.
The resultant of these two forces is $\mathbf{F}$.

   a) Find $\mathbf{F}$. *(2 marks)*

   b) Find the magnitude of $\mathbf{F}$. *(2 marks)*

   c) Find the acute angle between $\mathbf{F}$ and the unit vector $\mathbf{i}$. *(3 marks)*

5 A car travels along a straight road. When it passes a lamp post, the car is travelling at a speed of $6 \, \text{m s}^{-1}$. The car then moves with constant acceleration for 20 seconds and travels 300 metres.

a) Show that the acceleration of the car is $0.9 \, \text{m s}^{-2}$.   *(4 marks)*

b) Find the speed of the car at the end of the 20 seconds.   *(2 marks)*

c) The road is horizontal and the car has mass 1400 kg. A constant resistance force of 1500 N acts on the car while it is moving.
   i) Find the magnitude of the driving force that acts on the car while it is accelerating.   *(3 marks)*

   At the end of the 20 second period, the driving force is removed. The car then moves subject to the resistance force of 1500 N until it stops.
   ii) Find the distance that the car travels while it is slowing down.   *(5 marks)*

M1

6 A block, of mass 10 kg, is held at rest on a rough plane, which is inclined at an angle of 30° to the horizontal. The block is released and slides down the plane. The coefficient of friction between the block and the plane is 0.4.

a) Draw a diagram to show the forces acting on the block as it slides.   *(1 mark)*

b) Show that the magnitude of the friction acting on the block is approximately 33.9 N.   *(3 marks)*

c) Find the acceleration of the block.   *(4 marks)*

7 A girl throws a ball so that it passes through the centre of a netball hoop as shown in the diagram.

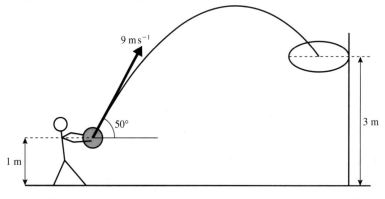

The ball is thrown from a height of 1 metre and the height of the hoop is 3 metres above the ground. The initial velocity of the ball is $9 \, \text{m s}^{-1}$ at an angle of 50° above the horizontal.

a) Find the maximum height of the ball above the ground.   *(4 marks)*

b) Find the time that it takes for the ball to reach the centre of the hoop.   *(6 marks)*

c) Find the horizontal distance from the initial position of the ball to the centre of the hoop.   *(2 marks)*

M1 Practice Paper (Option B)

90 minutes   75 marks   You may use a graphics calculator.

*Answer **all** questions.*

1 A stone is released from rest and falls vertically a distance of 40 metres before hitting the ground.

   a) Calculate the velocity of the stone as it hits the ground. *(2 marks)*

   b) Calculate the time between the stone being released and it hitting the ground. *(2 marks)*

   c) State one modelling assumption that you have made in order to answer the question. *(1 mark)*

2 a) A particle P moves with constant velocity. P passes through the points with position vectors $\begin{pmatrix} -1 \\ 4 \end{pmatrix}$ and $\begin{pmatrix} 7 \\ 8 \end{pmatrix}$ at times $t = 0$ and $t = 4$ respectively. Show that the velocity of P is $\begin{pmatrix} 2 \\ 1 \end{pmatrix}$ m s^{-1}. *(3 marks)*

   b) When $t = 4$, the particle P, of mass 3 kg, collides with a particle Q, of mass 2 kg. Immediately before the collision, Q is moving with velocity $\begin{pmatrix} 7 \\ -4 \end{pmatrix}$ m s^{-1}.

     As a result of the collision, P and Q coalesce into a single particle, R. Find the velocity of R immediately after the collision. *(4 marks)*

M1

3 The graph shows how the velocity, v m s^{-1}, of a train varies with time, t seconds, as it moves along a straight horizontal track between two stations. The journey takes 210 seconds.

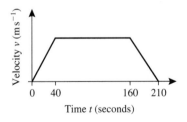

   a) The train starts from rest with a constant acceleration of 0.5 m s^{-2}. Find its maximum speed. *(2 marks)*

   b) Find the average speed of the train between the two stations. *(6 marks)*

4 Two forces, $\mathbf{F}_1 = 5\mathbf{i} + 12\mathbf{j}$ and $\mathbf{F}_2 = 7\mathbf{i} - 3\mathbf{j}$, act on a particle. The resultant of these two forces is $\mathbf{F}$.

   a) Find $\mathbf{F}$. *(2 marks)*

   b) Find the magnitude of $\mathbf{F}$. *(2 marks)*

   c) Find the acute angle between $\mathbf{F}$ and the unit vector $\mathbf{i}$. *(3 marks)*

5 Two particles, 3 kg and 7 kg, are connected by a light, inextensible string that passes over a smooth, light pulley. The two particles are released from rest, with the string taut, as shown in the diagram.

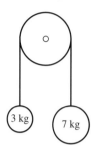

a) Show the acceleration of each particle is 3.92 m s^{-2}. (*5 marks*)

b) Calculate the tension in the string. (*2 marks*)

M1

6 A load of mass 20 kg is supported in equilibrium by two ropes. One rope is an angle of 30° to the vertical and the other rope is at 50° to the vertical, as shown in the diagram. The tensions in these ropes are T_1 and T_2 respectively.

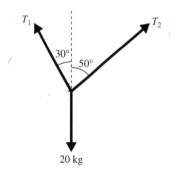

a) Show that $T_1 = 152 \text{ N}$, correct to 3 significant figures. (*3 marks*)

b) Find T_2. (*4 marks*)

7 A car travels along a straight road. When it passes a lamp post, the car is travelling at a speed of 6 m s^{-1}. The car then moves with constant acceleration for 20 seconds and travels 300 metres.

a) Show that the acceleration of the car is 0.9 m s^{-2}. (*4 marks*)

b) Find the speed of the car at the end of the 20 seconds. (*2 marks*)

c) The road is horizontal and the car has mass 1400 kg. A constant resistance force of 1500 N acts on the car while it is moving.

   i) Find the magnitude of the driving force that acts on the car while it is accelerating. (*3 marks*)

   At the end of the 20 second period, the driving force is removed. The car then moves subject to the resistance force of 1500 N until it stops.

   ii) Find the distance that the car travels while it is slowing down. (*5 marks*)

8 A block, of mass 10 kg, is held at rest on a rough plane, which is inclined at an angle of 30° to the horizontal. The block is released and slides down the plane. The coefficient of friction between the block and the plane is 0.4.

a) Draw a diagram to show the forces acting on the block as it slides.   (*1 mark*)

b) Show that the magnitude of the friction acting on the block is approximately 33.9 N.   (*3 marks*)

c) Find the acceleration of the block.   (*4 marks*)

9 A girl throws a ball so that it passes through the centre of a netball hoop, as shown in the diagram.

M1

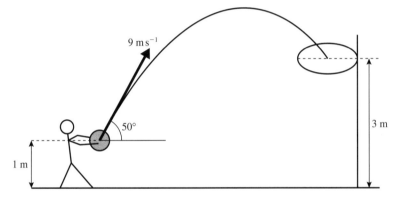

The ball is thrown from a height of 1 metre and the height of the hoop is 3 metres above the ground. The initial velocity of the ball is 9 m s⁻¹ at an angle of 50° above the horizontal.

a) Find the maximum height of the ball above the ground.   (*4 marks*)

b) Find the time that it takes for the ball to reach the centre of the hoop.   (*6 marks*)

c) Find the horizontal distance from the initial position of the ball to the centre of the hoop.   (*2 marks*)

7 Coursework guidance

This chapter is for students taking the M1A unit.

The M1B unit does not contain coursework.

If you are unsure which unit you are taking, you should ask your teacher.

In this chapter you will find:

◆ A clear definition of how to tackle the Mechanics coursework to meet the AQA specification.

◆ A strand by strand breakdown of the marking grid which will be used to assess your piece of work.

◆ Useful tips and hints from experienced moderators of the coursework.

◆ Answers to some frequently asked questions.

◆ A checklist to ensure that you have addressed all of the marking criteria.

7.1 Introduction

Mechanics coursework is an important aspect of AS-level mathematics, as it gives you the opportunity to demonstrate the skills that you have acquired by modelling a real-life problem. In the M1 module, you have studied theoretically topics such as Newton's laws of motion, friction and projectiles, but it is also necessary to look at these principles in action.

You will need to model a given task, make assumptions, define suitable variables and constants, perform relevant calculations, draw graphs, interpret your results and attempt to validate them by comparing them to real-life examples.

This chapter is to help you with the coursework process right from the starting point to handing in your completed piece of work. There will be useful hints and tips from experienced moderators who work for the Examination Board, as well as a clear and full description of the marking grid that will be used to assess your piece of work.

For your M1A coursework you will need to submit one task. This is worth $4\frac{1}{6}\%$ of the A-level marks available (or $8\frac{1}{3}\%$ if offered at AS-level).

The coursework process can be an enjoyable and rewarding experience. Hopefully, these guidelines will help you to produce a piece of work that you will be proud of. It will also help you to revise some of the topics that will appear on the final written paper.

7.2 Choosing a task

The AQA Examination Board will provide a list of tasks which are appropriate for your M1A coursework. Your teacher may decide to offer you one particular task or a number of tasks from which you

> Listen carefully to the advice of your teacher. **Do not** start a task that has not been approved by your teacher.

choose one. It is important to choose a task with which you feel comfortable and which gives you the opportunity to use your mechanics skills fully.

Your teacher may provide some time in class to discuss various ideas and approaches that you might take when tackling your task.

A good starting point is to have a brainstorming session, in which you should:

◆ Write down your ideas.
◆ Discuss these with others in your class.
◆ Adapt and modify your ideas and reject as necessary.

> This process will help you to clarify your thinking and ensure that you use a logical approach.

This discussion process is particularly important in mechanics, as the modelling process needs clear explanation to ensure that the correct and logical approach is taken.

7.3 The modelling process

The modelling process can be broken down into a series of stages, illustrated by this flowchart:

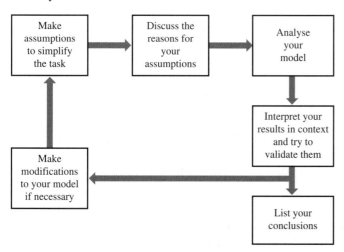

You should try to follow this process when conducting your coursework task.

7.4 Assessment criteria

Mechanics coursework is marked under four strands:

◆ Formulating the model
◆ Analysing the model
◆ Interpreting and validating the model
◆ Communication

There are 80 marks in total. The marking grid shows how the marks are allocated.

Strand	0–8 marks	9–15 marks	16–20 marks
1. Formulating the model	Problem defined and understood. Some simplifying assumptions made.	Assumptions stated and discussed and linked to a simple model. Appropriate choice of variables.	Comprehensive model set up. All assumptions clearly stated and discussed, where appropriate.
2. Analysing the model	Data collected and/or organised. Some accurate calculations and analysis of the problem.	Analyse the model using appropriate numerical and graphical or numerical and algebraic methods.	Analyse the comprehensive model. Clear and logical use of appropriate graphical or algebraic methods.
3. Interpreting and validating the model	Outcomes stated in everyday language. Some attempt to comment on the appropriateness of the numerical results.	Attempt to interpret and validate/or justify the solutions. Some limitations identified. Some consideration of refinements.	A reasoned attempt to interpret/validate/justify the solutions. Discussion of both limitations and refinements.
4. Communication	Some help given with the task if needed. Work clearly presented and organised.	Problem tackled with persistence and some initiative. Use of appropriate mathematical language or diagrams.	Coherent and logical approach to the task. Clear explanation of the findings/implications for further work.
			Total Mark Maximum 80

M1

The following section will discuss in detail the four strands that you will be assessed on. Reference will be made to the marking grid to help you understand exactly what is expected of you.

Strand 1: Formulating the model

You need to create a mathematical model which you can analyse. This will require you to make assumptions, discuss the reasons for them fully and then define variables and constants you will use in your analysis.

Candidates describe what they are going to investigate and how they hope to do it. They identify those problems to be modelled mathematically. **(4 marks)**

Once you have chosen your task you need to decide how you are going to tackle it.

Question: What particular aspect of the task are you going to develop?

A short introduction discussing what you are going to do and how you are going to do it is an excellent start. You can mention briefly which techniques you will be using and what extensions you will consider.

> **Do not** state in your aims that you are going to do something and then not bother to do it!

Any background information you can use to help with the introduction adds to the readability of the piece. You might use quoted sites from the Internet or reference books.

The piece of work will make all the necessary assumptions and discuss the reasons for them. (8 marks)

When looking to analyse a real-life situation, there are many different and complex factors that could potentially be included in your model. However, there is a danger that if you try to consider and incorporate everything that is relevant, you will end up with an over-complicated model which would be far too difficult to analyse.

If you were modelling an aeroplane taking off, you could consider many factors such as:

◆ The mass of the plane.
◆ The size of the plane.
◆ The effect of the wings.
◆ The contact between the wheels and the runway (including friction).
◆ The fuel load.
◆ Air resistance.
◆ Winds including crosswinds.
◆ The effect of gravity.
◆ The engine.
◆ Weather conditions.

You need to decide which factors are important. You can then discuss what you are going to assume about these factors and what their role will be in your model. Some factors can be assumed to have no effect for **your** model.

> Other students may include something you don't, and vice versa. There is no 'perfect', correct answer.

In many situations, it is appropriate to treat relatively large moving bodies as point masses. This simplifies the problem considerably.

Referring back to the aeroplane example, you might decide that its mass is important. You could then assume that the aeroplane is a particle, meaning that it will have mass but no size.

You need to consider all aspects that may affect your model and make appropriate assumptions accordingly. It is vital that you do not just make a list of assumptions with no discussion of them. You **must** explain in your own words why you have made these assumptions.

> As a guide, the assumptions and their explanations are worth 4 marks each.

Discuss what assumptions you would make in these cases:

◆ Modelling a stone being dropped/thrown down a well.
◆ Modelling a 100 m runner starting from the blocks.
◆ Modelling a high jumper clearing a height.

All assumptions should be sensible with either practical collection of data or evidence of research for them, where appropriate. (6 marks)

The assumptions you have made should be sensible and appropriate.

> If modelling a high jumper, it would not be sensible to assume $g = 0$. Also you might assume that the jumper is a particle, but is this sensible? One of the key aspects of high jumping is that the whole body needs to clear the bar and the 'shape' of it will be important.

There should be clear evidence of any research you have used to make assumptions. There is a wide range of websites on the Internet which give specific details and values you could use in your coursework.

M1

> If modelling a child's slide, you need values to use for the length of the slide and the materials used to make the slide. These could be obtained from appropriate websites (whose addresses should be stated). However, you might decide to obtain a value for μ to use in your analysis by performing an appropriate experiment using, for example, a block on an inclined plane covered in various fabrics.

If an experiment is used, the details should be given and the results clearly quoted. If a constant is needed, try to research its value rather than just guessing a value for it.

Remember that the experiment is to support your model, not to become the focus of the task. Your coursework is not a write-up of an experiment; it is a mathematical model of a real-life situation.

Suitable variables and constants should be defined fully. (2 marks)

Any variables or constants you will use in your analysis should be defined: for example, t = time in seconds.

> Units must be quoted for the full 2 marks.

Strand 2: Analysing the model

The calculations should be correct and appropriate to the model and the content of the unit. (10 marks)

You now need to analyse the model that you have set up.

You might look at simple numerical examples to illustrate your model or to help you to build up a table of values. It may be that you are calculating values of one variable as you change the value of another.

The calculations need to be accurate and you may decide to use a spreadsheet to help you. However, it is important that in your write-up you show clear evidence of at least one of each type of calculation that you use. Be careful, however, as nobody wants to trawl through page after page of repetitive calculations.

> Any 'extra' calculations could appear as an appendix at the back of your work.

You may then need to generalise your model to obtain algebraic formulae that can be graphed and interpreted.

Ensure that you have a sufficient range of calculations. For example, if you are analysing a child's slide, you need to consider the drop and then the run-off.

Candidates must either derive tables of values and use them to produce graphs and/or produce suitable algebraic formulae that they can use to both interpret and interpolate. **(8 marks)**

It is a good idea to tabulate any numerical results that you obtain, whether they are from calculations or derived from a formula. This will not only give you a feel for your results, but will hopefully flag up any obvious errors in your calculations.

You are expected as a minimum to either:

◆ obtain a table of values from calculations and then produce a graph from them, or
◆ obtain some generalised results and then interpret them.

Appropriate degrees of accuracy should have been used in the answers given. **(2 marks)**

Always think carefully about the answers that you give to ensure that they are appropriate for the values assumed earlier in your work. If you are consistent, you will obtain 1 mark. Work that is both fully appropriate and consistent will gain 2 marks.

> It is probably still a good idea to graph your algebraic expressions as they are then easier to interpret.

M1

Strand 3: Interpreting and validating the model

To address this strand you will look at your solutions and attempt to validate them. There is a tendency to spend too little time on this section, when it is worth the same amount of marks as the other three sections.

Candidates must predict what will happen to values of variables not calculated directly. These may be taken from a graph or formula and should be validated if possible. **(4 marks)**

You should be able to look at the formulae and graphs that you have obtained and make predictions from them.

Ask yourself the question: 'What would happen if … ?'

You may be able to make a prediction by:

◆ Changing a particular value in your general result.
◆ Using a graph that you have drawn.

They must look at how realistic their final results are, and, if appropriate, give reasons why the answers are not sensible.
(6 marks)

> For example, you might say that: 'For angles less than 40°, the graph shows that …'

You will have obtained a number of results.

Question: Are your results sensible and realistic?

To address this question, you could do one of the following:

✦ Carry out a practical experiment to test the results and predictions of your model.

✦ Compare your results with real-life examples of what you are modelling.

✦ Look for data on the Internet to confirm or contradict your results.

> If you are modelling a child's slide, look for examples in the local community.

Do not worry if your results are different from real-life examples. However, you should try to explain **why** your results are different. Is there any particular aspect or assumption that you made which could contribute to or be the major cause of the difference?

M1

They must look at the effects the assumptions have. This process should be done for all of the assumptions which directly affect the answer. They must look at what modifications could be made to the model in order to get a more realistic result (but they should not have to make them unless their model is so over-simplified that this becomes necessary).   **(10 marks)**

An important aspect of the interpretation of your model is to look back at your original assumptions and see what effects they had on the eventual solution that you obtained. For **each** individual assumption, discuss any difference there would be to your answer if that assumption had been changed.

It may be that you introduce something which had been ignored.

> In modelling an aeroplane taking off, you may have assumed that air resistance was negligible. You could state: 'If air resistance had been included, the total time taken would have increased because …'.

By making assumptions you usually make the task simpler. However, if your model is over-simplified it may become unworkable in reality.

You also need to suggest modifications that would provide a more realistic model. This is the opportunity to consider other aspects of the task which could have been looked at originally.

> If you are modelling a child's slide, you could have considered different shaped slides. You would not need to consider this modification in detail unless your original model was so simple that the analysis became trivial.

Strand 4: Communication

The final strand measures how well you have communicated your work in the write-up. This is a section which credits the good approaches used in the first three strands.

Candidates must express themselves clearly and concisely using appropriate mathematical language and notation. Graphs and diagrams should be clearly and accurately labelled.   **(4 marks)**

You will be assessed on how clearly you have expressed your ideas overall. It is important to be concise.

You do not need to include page after page of repetitive calculations, but you must include at least one worked example of all types of calculation that you have used in your coursework.

> There is no credit for producing the longest piece of coursework.

It is important to use the appropriate mathematical terms and notation. It is expected that in a piece of mechanics coursework there should be a force diagram drawn (if appropriate) with all relevant forces shown.

Candidates should include other areas of work which could have been investigated further.   **(2 marks)**

You are expected to suggest other work that could follow from your coursework.

> Do not confuse 'further work' with 'modifications'.

M1

Question: Where could you take your research further?

> If you were modelling a child's slide, you could look at a waterslide or a toboggan as alternatives to a slide.

The final conclusions should be set out logically.   **(2 marks)**

Your final conclusions should be stated clearly at the end of your coursework.

Question: What exactly did your analysis indicate?

The overall piece of work should be of sufficient depth and difficulty.   **(6 marks)**

This section gives credit for all of the work that has been done throughout your coursework. Ensure that your approaches have enabled you to generate enough mathematics for you to have shown the appropriate skills from the unit.

You will receive credit not only for the difficulty of your calculation, but for the quality and depth of your interpretation and for your overall approach.

> It is not expected that you will be looking for ways to make the coursework artificially difficult.

The investigation should form a coherent whole and should be of a length consistent with a piece of work of 8–10 hours.   **(6 marks)**

Your report should read as a logical piece of writing that should be easy to follow. If you struggle to follow the flow of your arguments when reading the work through, then so will the person marking and assessing it. It is expected that your piece of work will take 8–10 hours to complete. This is an approximate timing and includes data collection and write-up time. It is easy to get carried away with some tasks, so be careful that your piece of work does not become too long.

> It is not expected that you will use the strands as specific titles in your coursework, although it should be clear to the reader which strand is being addressed.

When complete, read through your work and check your calculations to ensure that you have not made any careless mistakes.

7.5 Frequently asked questions

Here are some questions that are often asked by students.

◆ **Should the coursework be handwritten or word-processed?**

It can be either. If handwritten, try to ensure that the work is neat and clear to follow. If word-processed, take care when typing symbols.

◆ **How long should the piece of work be?**

An appropriate piece of work could vary from 10 sides up to 20 sides including diagrams.

> Word-processed pieces tend to be shorter.

◆ **Should I label the page numbers?**

Yes. It is useful when the work is being moderated.

◆ **Can I use the Internet?**

Yes. The Internet is appropriate to collect relevant information on your task, and it will be useful to obtain constants you may need for your model. **Always** quote any websites used.

> Any attempt to copy work from the Internet is against Examination Board rules and could lead to serious consequences.

Make sure that you are aware of the deadline set by your teacher and work to it.

7.6 Checklist

Have you …?

Strand 1

◆ Stated your aims clearly.

◆ Listed your assumptions and discussed the reasons for them.

◆ Ensured your assumptions are sensible and listed any sources of information such as websites.

◆ Provided clear details of any experiments used to collect data practically.

◆ Defined all variables and constants with appropriate units.

Strand 2

◆ Checked the accuracy of your calculations.

◆ Ensured that you have a full range of appropriate calculations.

◆ Ensured that you have produced tables of values or algebraic formulae and graphs.

◆ Used appropriate degrees of accuracy in your answers.

Strand 3

◆ Made predictions for values of variables not calculated directly.

◆ Looked at how realistic your final results are and if not have you tried to give reasons.

◆ Looked at the effect of all the assumptions made on your results and suggested modifications that could be made to your model.

Strand 4

◆ Expressed yourself clearly using diagrams and appropriate mathematical language and notation.

◆ Suggested other areas of work that could have been considered.

◆ Set our your final conclusions clearly.

◆ Made sure your work is of sufficient depth and difficulty. (Have you made it too simplistic?)

◆ Made sure your work is easy to follow and of sufficient length.

M1

Answers

Chapter 1

Check out

1 To simplify the equations. In practice, the flow rate will be different at different distances from the bank

2 The shell is a particle. Air resistance is zero. Gravity is constant

Revision exercise 1

1 a) Yes b) Probably not c) No d) Yes e) Probably f) Yes g) Yes h) No

2 a) Yes b) No c) No d) Yes

2 e) No, in the sense that friction is needed for there to be a forward force at the wheels driving the car forward

2 f) No, because in addition to e) there must be a friction force towards the centre of curvature causing the car to change direction

Chapter 2

Check in

1 3   **2** 88   **3** 3.30 or -0.303 **4** 5.39 cm   **5** a) $21.8°$ b) i) 10.4 cm ii) 6.71 cm

Exercise 2A

1 a) i) $15\,\mathrm{m\,s^{-1}}$ ii) $126\,\mathrm{km\,h^{-1}}$ b) i) $81.8\,\mathrm{km\,h^{-1}}$ ii) $22.7\,\mathrm{m\,s^{-1}}$ **2** $3\,\mathrm{km\,h^{-1}}$ **3** a) $9\,\mathrm{km\,h^{-1}}$ b) $2\frac{1}{4}\,\mathrm{h}$ c) $8.47\,\mathrm{km\,h^{-1}}$

4 a) $22\frac{2}{9}\,\mathrm{m\,s^{-1}}$ b) The first stage takes $100\,\mathrm{s}$ and to average $40\,\mathrm{m\,s^{-1}}$ the whole journey would have to be done in this time

5 a) $20\,\mathrm{km\,h^{-1}}$ b) $5\frac{5}{9}\,\mathrm{m\,s^{-1}}$ **6** a) $7.58\,\mathrm{km\,h^{-1}}$ b) $12\,\mathrm{km\,h^{-1}}$ **7** $90\,\mathrm{km\,h^{-1}}$ **8** $58\frac{1}{3}\,\mathrm{km\,h^{-1}}$

Exercise 2B

1 a)

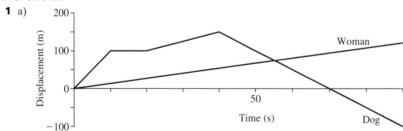

1 b) Pass after $54.7\,\mathrm{s}$, $76.6\,\mathrm{m}$ from A   c) Average speed $4\frac{4}{9}\,\mathrm{m\,s^{-1}}$, average velocity $-1\frac{1}{9}\,\mathrm{m\,s^{-1}}$

2 a), b)

2 c) Pass after $1\,\mathrm{h}\,48\frac{1}{3}\,\mathrm{min}$, $31\frac{1}{9}\,\mathrm{km}$ from A

3 a) Constant speed of $5\,\mathrm{km\,h^{-1}}$ for $2\,\mathrm{h}$, stationary for $1\,\mathrm{h}$, return to start at $3\frac{1}{3}\,\mathrm{km\,h^{-1}}$

3 b)

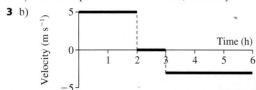

4 a)

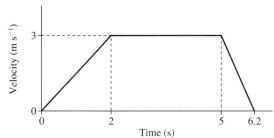

Assumes constant acceleration and instantaneous changes of acceleration

4 b) 13.8 m

5

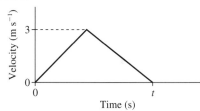

The journey takes 7.2 s

6 a)

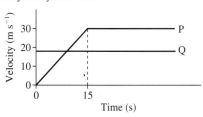

6 b) 75 m   c) 7.5 s

7 a)

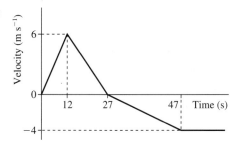

7 b) 81 m   c) 7.5 s

8 a) 5 min 30 s

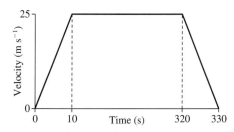

8 b) Maximum 7 min 33.6 s, when limit starts more than 125 m from Chulchit's home and ends more than 230 m from his work; minimum 7 min 28.8 s, when limit starts at Chulchit's home or ends at his work

Exercise 2C

1 a) 1350 m b) 90 m s⁻¹ **2** a) 10 m s⁻² b) 125 m **3** a) 3 m s⁻² b) 30 m s⁻¹ **4** 7392 m **5** 0.139 m s⁻², 0.069 m s⁻²

6 a) $23\frac{5}{6}$ m b) $3\frac{2}{3}$ s **7** $a = 3.2$ m s⁻² **8** 35.5 s **9** 15 m **10** a) 5 s b) 25 m **11** Henry stops 19.375 m behind Clare.

Exercise 2D

1 a) 3.19 s b) 31.3 m s⁻¹ **2** a) 11.5 m b) 1.53 s c) 3.06 s **3** a) 19.8 m s⁻¹ b) 4.04 (total time in air)

3 c) 19.8 m s⁻¹ downwards **4** a) 1.28 m above top of cliff b) −34.7 m s⁻¹ c) 4.05 s **5** a) 3.88 m b) 1.52 s **6** 45 m

7 Time 4 s, height 8g m **8** $\frac{5}{16}$ m above top of window **9** $V = h − 5.5g$ **10** $\dfrac{u}{g} − \dfrac{t}{2}$

Exercise 2E

1 a) i) $p + \frac{1}{2}q$ ii) $\frac{1}{2}q − p$ iii) $q − p$ **2** a) 2q b) p + q c) q − 2p d) 2q − 2p e) p − 2q

3 a) 2q b) p + q c) −q d) 2q − p e) $\frac{1}{2}p + 1\frac{1}{2}q$ f) $\frac{1}{2}p − 1\frac{1}{2}q$

5 a) i) $−\frac{1}{2}q$ ii) $−p − \frac{1}{2}q$ iii) $\frac{1}{3}(q − p)$ iv) $\frac{1}{6}(q − p)$, showing that B, G and E colinear

7 a) 7.02 km, 098.9° b) 23.4 km, 217.3° c) 23.5 km h⁻¹, 290.6° d) 529.1 N, 347.5°

8 a) $\overrightarrow{AB} = \overrightarrow{OB} − \overrightarrow{OA}$ b) i) 20.6 km, 140.9° ii) 61.8 km, 140.9° iii) 20.6t km, 140.9° c) 5.82 h (5 h 49 min)

8 d) 10.49 h (10 h 29 min) **9** a) 5.385 m s⁻¹, 80 m downstream from B b) Steer upstream at 23.6° to AB, 4.583 m s⁻¹

10 a) 408 km h⁻¹, on bearing 078.7° b) bearing 101.5°, 392 km h⁻¹ **11** 6 km h⁻¹, 10.4 km h⁻¹

Exercise 2F

1 a) 2j b) −2i − 2j c) −6i + 7j d) 16i + j e) √5 f) 2√5 **2** a) $u = −10, v = −1$ b) $u = −3.5$

3 a) −12i + 16j b) −0.6i + 0.8j **4** a) 5.803i + 3.914j b) 1.996i + 9.39j c) 10.064i + 6.536j d) 4j e) −3.638i + 7.46j

4 f) −10.143i + 21.751j g) −3.556i + 5.079j h) 12.474i + 6.536j i) −2.057i − 2.832j

5 a) 5.385, 21.8° b) 11.402, 52.12° c) 5, −90° d) 3.606, 123.69° e) 5.831, −59.04° f) 7.81, −140.19° g) 2, 180°

6 a) $\overrightarrow{OA} = 19.021i + 6.18j$, $\overrightarrow{AB} = 11.389i + 25.579j$ b) $\overrightarrow{OB} = 30.41i + 31.76j$ c) 43.97 km, 043.8°

7 a) $\overrightarrow{OA} = −34.468i + 6.078j$, $\overrightarrow{OB} = 25i + 43.301j$ b) $\overrightarrow{AB} = \overrightarrow{OB} − \overrightarrow{OA} = 59.468i + 37.224j$ c) 70.157 km. 058° **8** a) √5 m s⁻¹

8 b) A at 63.435°, B at 18.435° to x-direction, angle between 45° c) $\overrightarrow{OA} = ti + 2tj$, $\overrightarrow{OB} = 3ti + tj$, $\overrightarrow{AB} = 2ti − tj$ d) 40.25 s

Exercise 2G

1 a) (34i + 18j) m s⁻¹ b) 38.5 m s⁻¹ at 27.9° to the x-direction c) (144i + 48j) m **2** a) .(i + j) m s⁻² b) (36i + 6j) m c) 36.5 m

3 Speed changes from 2√10 to 4√10 m s⁻¹, directions are tan⁻¹ 3 and tan⁻¹(−⅓), which are perpendicular

4 Velocity (10i − 3j) ms⁻¹, displacement (28i + 4j) m

5 Velocity $v = (35i + 49j)$ m s⁻¹, position $r = (40i + 56j)$ m, $r = \dfrac{8}{g}v$, so directions are the same. Speed = 60.2 m s⁻¹

6 a) $\overrightarrow{OP} = 2t(60 − t)i + 4(100 − t^2)j$ b) 10 s c) 1000 m **7** a) $a = (26i − 68j)/15$, $u = (−41i + 38j)/15$

8 a) (4i + 6j) m b) (8i − 15j) m s⁻¹ c) (−2i + 3.75j) m s⁻² d) (50i + 60j) m s

Check out

1 Displacement is a vector comprising distance plus direction **2** 36 km h⁻¹

3 a) 80 m b) −20 m c) 1.5 m s⁻¹, −2 m s⁻¹ d) $−\frac{4}{9}$ m s⁻¹ **4** a) 0.6 m s⁻² b) 240 m c) 150 m

5 $v = u + at$, $s = \frac{1}{2}(u + v)t$, $s = ut + \frac{1}{2}at^2$, $s = vt − \frac{1}{2}at^2$, $v^2 = u^2 + 2as$ **6** a) 4 m s⁻² b) 90 m **7** 6.39 s

8

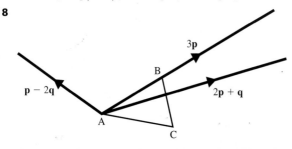

9 a) 12i − 16j b) 12i + 7j c) −7i − 29j **10** 3.06i + 2.57j **11** a) 6.71 b) −26.6° to x-direction

12 $v = u + at$, $r = \frac{1}{2}(u + v)t$, $r = ut + \frac{1}{2}at^2$, $r = vt − \frac{1}{2}at^2$ **13** a) $r = (13.5i + 12j)$ m

Revision exercise 2

1 a) $6.5\,\mathrm{m\,s^{-1}}$ b) $22.6°$ **2** b) 0.75 c) $53.1°$ **3** a) $68.8\,\mathrm{m}$ b) i) $200\,\mathrm{s}$ ii) $66.7\,\mathrm{s}$ **4** b) $2.5\,\mathrm{m\,s^{-1}}$ c) $53°$

5 a) $9\mathbf{i} - 4\mathbf{j}$ b) $9.85\,\mathrm{N}$ c) $24.0°$

6 a) $21\,\mathrm{m\,s^{-1}}$ b) $2.14\,\mathrm{s}$ d) No air resistance, or object is a particle, or acceleration is constant

7 a) $0.625\,\mathrm{m\,s^{-2}}, 0, -0.41\dot{7}\,\mathrm{m\,s^{-2}}$ b) $32.5\,\mathrm{m}$ c) cyclist, $5\,\mathrm{s}$

7 d) No, provided you always measure to the same point on the cyclist and car

8 a) $2.4\,\mathrm{m\,s^{-1}}$ c) $1.89\,\mathrm{m\,s^{-1}}$ **9** a) i) Graph is a straight line ii) $\frac{2}{3}\mathrm{m\,s^{-2}}$ b) $21\,\mathrm{s}$

10 a) i) $3\mathbf{i}\,\mathrm{m\,s^{-1}}$ b) $(3 + 0.1t)\mathbf{i} + 0.2t\mathbf{j}\,\mathrm{m\,s^{-1}}$ d) $89.4\,\mathrm{m}$ **11** a) i) $\dfrac{2U}{3}\,\mathrm{m\,s^{-2}}$ ii) $12U\,\mathrm{m}$ b) $2\,\mathrm{m\,s^{-1}}$

12 a) $(1.2\mathbf{i} + 0.8\mathbf{j})\,\mathrm{m\,s^{-2}}$ b) $405\mathbf{i} + 90\mathbf{j}$ **13** a) $4\,\mathrm{s}, 5.6\,\mathrm{s}$ b) $50\,\mathrm{m}$ c) $58\,\mathrm{m}$ d) $12.5\,\mathrm{m\,s^{-2}}$, which is greater than g

13 e) Acceleration would not be constant, hence graph would not be linear

14 b) $46.6\,\mathrm{m}$ c) $4\,\mathrm{s}$ **15** a) $(40\mathbf{i} - 5\mathbf{j})\,\mathrm{m}$ b) $(3\mathbf{i} - \mathbf{j})\,\mathrm{m\,s^{-1}}$ c) $(\mathbf{i} - 2\mathbf{j})\,\mathrm{m\,s^{-1}}$ d) $(10\mathbf{i} - 20\mathbf{j})\,\mathrm{m}$

Chapter 3

Check in

1 Beam is rigid, strings are light and inextensible, brick is a particle   **2** $AC = 6.13\,\mathrm{cm}, BC = 5.14\,\mathrm{cm}$ **3** $x = 4, y = 3$

4 $F = 3.73, R = 18.6, P = 3.97$ **5** a) $x \geqslant 7$ b) $x \geqslant -2$

Exercise 3A

1 a)

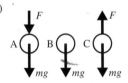

b)

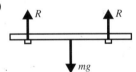

c)

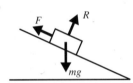

1 d)

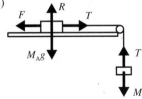

e)

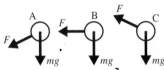

f)

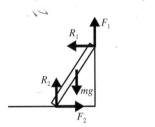

2 a)

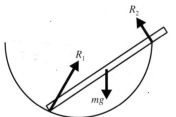

b) $T = M_B g, F = M_B g$ **3** a)

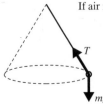

b)

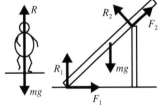

5

6 If air resistance included, it would act tangentially to circle

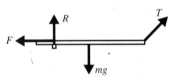

7   Friction $F = 3g$ N

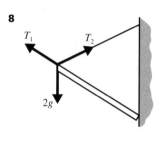

8

Exercise 3B

1 a) Resultant: $(4.312\mathbf{i} + 4.095\mathbf{j})$ N or 5.497 N at 43.5° to x-direction
   Equilibrant: $(4.312\mathbf{i} + 4.095\mathbf{j})$ N or 5.497 N at $-136.5°$ to x-direction

1 b) Resultant: $(-1.186\mathbf{i} + 2.981\mathbf{j})$ N or 3.208 N at 111.7° to x-direction
   Equilibrant: $(-1.186\mathbf{i} + 2.981\mathbf{j})$ N or 3.208 N at $-68.3°$ to x-direction

1 c) Resultant: $(-1.793P\mathbf{i} + 0.109P\mathbf{j})$ N or 1.796P N at 176.5° to x-direction
   Equilibrant: $(-1.793P\mathbf{i} + 0.109P\mathbf{j})$ N or 1.796P N at $-3.5°$ to x-direction

2 a) $P = 9.178$ N, $Q = 9.664$ N   b) $P = 7.660$ N, $Q = 6.732$ N   c) $P = -3.230$ N, $Q = -12.102$ N

3 a) $P = 12.856$ N, $Q = 15.321$ N   b) $P = 9.434$ N, $\theta = 122°$ c) $P = 17.174$ N, $Q = 15.827$ N   **4** As Question 3

5 a) $P = 2.536$ N, $Q = 5.438$ N   b) $P = 17.341$ N, $Q = 24.508$ N   c) $P = 17.264$ N, $Q = 24.045$ N

6 9.95 N, 15.2 N   **7** $F = 30.2$ N, $R = 82.9$ N

8 a) $T = \dfrac{P\sqrt{3}}{2}, R = \tfrac{1}{2}(392 - P)$ b) The block would lift off the ground

9 60.058 N, 50.395 N   **10** a) $P = 16\tfrac{1}{3}$ N, $T = 42.467$ N   b) 15.077 N, $T = 36.185$ N

11 a) 17.925 N, 25.313 N   b) $P = 5.597$ N, $T = 22.403$ N   **12** $P = \dfrac{Wb}{a}$ **13** $\dfrac{Wb}{a}$

Exercise 3C

1 a) 0.408   b) 0.321   c) 0.294   d) 0.641   e) 0.619   f) 0.379

2 a) 23.5 N   b) 35.1 N   c) 32.0 N   d) 29.2 N   e) 52.1 N   f) 54.5 N

3 22.2 N, 0.51   **5** a) 18.4 N   b) 4.77 N   **6** 49.3 N   **7** 34.9°   **8** a) 18.9 N   b) 0.482   **9** 0.36

Check out

1 Internal force in a rod resisting external forces pushing in on its ends.

2

R

5 N

F

20°

8g N

or

R

5 N

20°

F

8g N

3 32.0 N, 43.1 N

4 0.128

5 Max $F = 36.9$ N, but force parallel to slope is 43.3 N, so block moves

Revision exercise 3

1 b) 283 **2** a) $p = -400\,\text{N}, q = 680\,\text{N}$ b) Cable 2 is most likely to break **3** a) $21.7\mathbf{i} + 12.5\mathbf{j}$ b) $-7.5\mathbf{i} - 26.6\mathbf{j}$

5 a) 61.8 N b) 8.16 kg **6** b) 3.46 N

7 a)

c) 75 N d) $82\frac{1}{2}$ **8** a)

c) $k = 0.197$

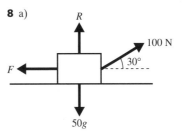

Chapter 4

Check in

1 $\mathbf{p} = 4\mathbf{i} + 6\mathbf{j}$ **2** Pulley is smooth and light, string is light and inextensible, air resistance is zero

3 Horizontal 49.1 N, vertical 34.4 N **4** 78.4 N

Exercise 4A

1 $2.25\,\text{m s}^{-2}$ **2** 52.5 N **3** $6\frac{2}{3}\,\text{kg}$ **4** $(3\mathbf{i} + 4.5\mathbf{j})\,\text{m s}^{-2}$ **5** $(6\mathbf{i} - 15\mathbf{j})\,\text{N}$ **6** a) $0.8\,\text{m s}^{-2}$ b) 400 kg c) 380 N

6 d) 1290 N e) $-0.4\,\text{m s}^{-2}$ **7** a) $12\,\text{m s}^{-1}$ b) 99 m **8** $(0.75\mathbf{i} + 1.25\mathbf{j})\,\text{m s}^{-2}$ **9** $P = (-\mathbf{i} - \mathbf{j})$ **10** $5\sqrt{13}\,\text{N}$

11 702.4 N **12** a) $9.50\,\text{m s}^{-2}$ at $51.2°$ to x-direction b) $11.8\,\text{m s}^{-2}$ at $100.7°$ to x-direction **13** a) 539 N b) $15.6\,\text{m s}^{-2}$

14 $0.725\,\text{m s}^{-2}$ on bearing $073.3°$

Exercise 4B

1 a) i) $2.7\,\text{m s}^{-2}$ upwards ii) $2.3\,\text{m s}^{-2}$ downwards b) i) 196 N ii) 196 N iii) 236 N iv) $182\frac{2}{3}\,\text{N}$ v) 241 N

2 a) 2640 N, 440 N b) 4200 N, 440 N **3** a) 550 N b) 490 N c) 452.5 N d) 390 N

4 a) 13.1 kg b) 92.2 kg c) 73.5 kg d) 80 kg e) 72.5 kg **5** $1.96\,\text{m s}^{-2}$ upwards **6** a) $3.07\,\text{m s}^{-2}$ b) 59.2 N

7 $4.04\,\text{m s}^{-2}$ **8** 0.306 **9** 14.6 m **10** Stage 1: 18.7 N; stage 2: 14.7 N; stage 3: -9.3 N **11** 0.092 **12** $10.8\,\text{m s}^{-1}$

13 67.7 N **8** 0.306 **14** a) 17.8 N b) 21.7 N c) 17.7 N **15** 4.59 m, particle remains at rest **16** $0.855\,\text{m s}^{-2}$

17 a) $5.49\,\text{m s}^{-1}$ b) $12.9\,\text{m s}^{-1}$

Exercise 4C

1 a) 39.2 N, 68.6 N b) 39.2 N, 68.6 N c) 51.2 N, 89.6 N **2** a) 90.4 N, 56.5 N b) $5.2\,\text{m s}^{-2}$, top string breaks

3 a) $1\,\text{m s}^{-2}$, 1500 N b) 1200 N c) 136.4 N **4** a) 45.8 N b) 29.5 N **5** a) 1.63 N b) 57.2 N c) 114 N

6 $1.96\,\text{m s}^{-2}$, $3.96\,\text{m s}^{-1}$ **7** $3.27\,\text{m s}^{-2}$, $13.1m$ N **8** $3.92\,\text{m s}^{-2}$, 11.8 N **9** $3.22\,\text{m s}^{-2}$, 32.9 N **10** $5.88\,\text{m s}^{-2}$, 0.714 s

11 $2.285\,\text{m s}^{-2}$, 22.55 N **12** a) $4.2\,\text{m s}^{-2}$ b) $5.02\,\text{m s}^{-1}$ c) 1.29 m **13** a) $0.891\,\text{m s}^{-2}$ b) 17.8 N

Check out

1 1st law: An object has constant velocity unless there is a resultant external force acting on it
2nd law: Acceleration is proportional to resultant force (assuming mass is constant), leading to $\mathbf{F} = m\mathbf{a}$
3rd law: For every action there is an equal and opposite reaction

2 $2\mathbf{i} + 2\mathbf{j}$ **3** a) 4545 N b) 505 N **4** $5.88\,\text{m s}^{-2}$, 31.4 N **5** a) 1345 N b) 245 N

Revision exercise 4

1 a) i) 48 m b) 600 N **2** b) 880 m d) i) 600 N ii) 3600 N **3** a) $-10\mathbf{i} - 5\mathbf{j}$ b) 19.9 N **4** a) ii) 3.36 N b) 2.8 m

5 b) 0.4 b) 6.74 N **6** b) 31.35 N **7** a) i) 25 N thrust ii) 150 N b) 100 N **8** b) $32\,\text{m s}^{-1}$

8 c) i) 4680 N ii) $341\frac{1}{3}$ m **9** a) ii) 470.4 N b) 2.4 m **10** $0.98\,\text{m s}^{-2}$, 17.6 N

11 b) 38 N c) 36.2 N d) 0.62 **12** b) i) 679 N c) $2.35\,\text{m s}^{-2}$ **13** b) $0.8\,\text{m s}^{-2}$ c) 1.8 N d) $t = 125$ s

14 a) ii) 115.8 N b) $1.20\,\text{m s}^{-2}$ c) Sledge is a particle, no air resistance

Chapter 5
Check in
1 i) Vector ii) Vector iii) Scalar   **2** $v = \frac{1}{7}i + \frac{2}{7}j$

Exercise 5A
1 $3.97\,\text{m s}^{-1}$ **2** a) $3.2\,\text{m s}^{-1}$ b) $0.8\,\text{m s}^{-1}$ **3** $0.45\,\text{kg}$ **4** a) $\dfrac{10v}{7}$ b) $\dfrac{2v}{7}$

5 a) $4\frac{2}{3}\,\text{m s}^{-1}$ b) If $m > 4$, A's velocity is greater than B's, so A would need to 'pass through' B

6 $\frac{9}{14}\,\text{m s}^{-1}$ **7** a) $15\,\text{m s}^{-1}$ b) $6000\,\text{N}$ **8** $717\,\text{m s}^{-1}$ **9** $3.6\,\text{m s}^{-1}$ **10** $2\,\text{m s}^{-1}$ **11** $3600\,\text{N}$

12 $(3.2i + 3.2j)\,\text{m s}^{-1}$ **13** $-8j\,\text{m s}^{-1}$ **14** $(5i + j)\,\text{m s}^{-1}$ **15** $m = 2, a = -5$

Check out
1 a) $24\,\text{N s}$ b) $(20i - 10j)\,\text{N s}$ **2** a) $(4.4i + 3.8j)\,\text{m s}^{-1}$ b) Direction reversed; speed $4\,\text{m s}^{-1}$

Revision exercise 5
1 $1\,\text{m s}^{-1}$ **2** b) 18.6 **3** 0.4 **4** a) $\begin{pmatrix} -3 \\ 4 \end{pmatrix}$ b) $5\,\text{m s}^{-1}$ **5** a) 0.025 b) 4 **6** a) $0.8\,\text{m s}^{-1}$ c) $40\,\text{N}$

7 a) $28.4\,\text{m s}^{-1}$ b) $1.14\,\text{m s}^{-1}$ c) $0.110\,\text{m}$ **8** a) $8\,\text{m s}^{-1}$ b) i) $19.6\,\text{N}$ ii) $16.3\,\text{m}$

Chapter 6
Check in
1 $y = 36.9685$, or 37.0 to 3 sf   **2** $51.5°$ **3** 4.32 or -0.236

Exercise 6A
1 a) $1.76\,\text{s}$ b) $21.6\,\text{m}$ c) $0.878\,\text{s}$ d) $3.78\,\text{m}$ **2** a) $1.77\,\text{s}$ b) $8.84\,\text{m}$ c) $0.884\,\text{s}$ d) $3.83\,\text{m}$

3 a) $17.2\,\text{m}$ b) $15.4\,\text{m s}^{-1}$ c) $2.5°$ below horizontal   **4** a) $(30i + 35.1j)\,\text{m}$ at $t = 1\,\text{s}$, $(60i + 60.4j)\,\text{m}$ at $t = 2\,\text{s}$ b) $8.16\,\text{s}$ c) $245\,\text{m}$

5 $30°$ **6** $31.3\,\text{m s}^{-1}$ **7** $20.5\,\text{m s}^{-1}$, $15.4\,\text{m s}^{-1}$, $25.6\,\text{m s}^{-1}$, $36.9°$ to horizontal

8 a) $h = \dfrac{V^2\sin^2 40°}{19.6}$ b) $21.8\,\text{m s}^{-1}$ c) $47.7\,\text{m}$ d) Ball is a particle, no air resistance   **9** $95.8\,\text{m}$

10 a) $\frac{1}{7}\,\text{s}$ b) $0.1\,\text{m}$ c) $1.67°$ below the horizontal   **12** a) Gradient $= \dfrac{\sin\theta - \sin\alpha}{\cos\theta - \cos}$ b) Rate of increase $= u\sqrt{2(1 - \cos(\theta - \alpha))}$

Check out
1 $u\cos\alpha\,i + (u\sin\alpha - gt)j$ **2** $2.35\,\text{s}$ **3** $6.74\,\text{m}$ **4** $22.6\,\text{m}$ **5** a) $2.29\,\text{s}$ b) $21.0\,\text{m}$ **6** $900y = 600x - 4.9x^2$

Revision exercise 6
1 a) $40.2\,\text{m}$ b) $42.5\,\text{m}$ **2** a) $16.9\,\text{m}$ b) $39.0\,\text{m}$ c) $10.5\,\text{m s}^{-1}$ **3** b) $39.2\,\text{m}$ c) i) $12.0\,\text{m s}^{-1}$ ii) Horizontal

4 b) i) $12.5\,\text{m s}^{-1}$ c) $13.9\,\text{m}$ **5** b) Under the top c) $9.57\,\text{m s}^{-1}$ **6** a) ii) $26\,\text{m s}^{-1}$ **7** c) $82\,\text{m}$

8 b) i) $3.03\,\text{m}$ ii) $0.714\,\text{s}$ iii) $1.57\,\text{s}$

M1 Practice Paper (Option A)
1 a) $28\,\text{m s}^{-1}$ b) $2.86\,\text{s}$ **2** b) $\begin{pmatrix} 4 \\ -1 \end{pmatrix}\,\text{m s}^{-1}$ **3** a) $20\,\text{m s}^{-1}$ b) $15.7\,\text{m s}^{-1}$

4 a) $12i \div 9j$ b) 15 c) $36.9°$ **5** b) $24\,\text{m s}^{-1}$ c) i) $2670\,\text{N}$ ii) $269\,\text{m}$

6 a)   c) $1.51\,\text{m s}^{-2}$ **7** a) $3.43\,\text{m}$ b) $0.998\,\text{s}$ c) $5.77\,\text{m}$

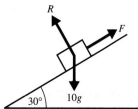

M1 Practice Paper (Option B)

1 a) $28\,\mathrm{m\,s^{-1}}$ b) $2.86\,\mathrm{s}$ c) No air resistance or stone is a particle   **2** b) $\begin{pmatrix} 4 \\ -1 \end{pmatrix}$ **3** a) $20\,\mathrm{m\,s^{-1}}$ b) $15.7\,\mathrm{m\,s^{-1}}$

4 a) $12\mathbf{i} + 9\mathbf{j}$ b) 15 c) $36.9°$ **5** b) $41.16\,\mathrm{N}$ **6** b) $99.5\,\mathrm{N}$ **7** b) $24\,\mathrm{m\,s^{-1}}$ c) i) $2760\,\mathrm{N}$ ii) $268.8\,\mathrm{m}$

8 a)   c) $1.51\,\mathrm{m\,s^{-2}}$ **9** a) $3.43\,\mathrm{m}$ b) $0.998\,\mathrm{s}$ c) $5.77\,\mathrm{m}$

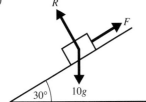

Formulae

You should learn the following formulae, which are **not** included in the AQA formulae booklet, but which may be required to answer questions.

Constant Acceleration Formulae	$s = ut + \frac{1}{2}at^2$ $\qquad$ $\mathbf{s} = \mathbf{u}t + \frac{1}{2}\mathbf{a}t^2$
	$s = vt - \frac{1}{2}at^2$ $\qquad$ $\mathbf{s} = \mathbf{v}t - \frac{1}{2}\mathbf{a}t^2$
	$v = ut + at$ $\qquad$ $\mathbf{v} = \mathbf{u} + \mathbf{a}t$
	$s = \frac{1}{2}(u + v)t$ $\qquad$ $\mathbf{s} = \frac{1}{2}(\mathbf{u} + \mathbf{v})t$
	$v^2 = u^2 + 2as$
Weight	$W = mg$
Momentum	Momentum $= mv$
Newton's Second Law	$F = ma$ $\quad$ or $\quad$ Force = Rate of change of momentum
Friction, dynamic	$F = \mu N$
Friction, static	$F \leqslant \mu N$

Index